Directions: Print the capital and small letters of the alphabet.

Can you print the **ABC**'s?

A a

LESSON 1: Alphabetical sequence

1

Directions: Print the letter that comes between the given letters.

m ___ o   t ___ v   d ___ f

a ___ c   p ___ r   l ___ n

g ___ i   b ___ d   r ___ t

o ___ q   s ___ u   u ___ w

x ___ z   j ___ l   v ___ x

Directions: Print the letters that come before and after the given letters.

___ k ___   ___ w ___   ___ e ___

___ s ___   ___ o ___   ___ q ___

___ d ___   ___ h ___   ___ v ___

___ m ___   ___ x ___   ___ c ___

___ i ___   ___ t ___   ___ b ___

Directions: Begin at the ★ and follow the alphabet from dot to dot to form a letter. Find the letter, capital and small, in the words. Circle the letter each time you find it.

a b e f	Happy	d e g h	something
	hello		make
c d	birthday	f	rain
j i	surprise	m k	Some
	Here		Must
l k h g	Mother	l	Name
		o n j i	

m n		p q s t	
	look		Nuts
	Little		know
	Hello	w	children
o p	milk	r	farm
	Sally		new
r q	will	y x v u	soon

s t		u v x y	
	Wants		Live
	letters		loves
z y v u	help	w	Vine
	Tom		every
	went		went
x w	Time	z	ever

Directions: Print the missing letters of the alphabet.

c ___	h ___	j ___	k ___	e ___
k ___	n ___	p ___	i ___	b ___
d ___	c ___	e ___	c ___	g ___
q ___	r ___	t ___	w ___	m ___
n ___	p ___	r ___	y ___	x ___
p ___	s ___	u ___	r ___	o ___
y ___	d ___	f ___	v ___	s ___
s ___	b ___	d ___	z ___	n ___
w ___	k ___	m ___	f ___	q ___

Directions: Print the missing small letters to complete the alphabet.

a ___ ___ ___ ___ f ___ ___ i

___ k ___ ___ ___ ___ q ___

___ u ___ ___ ___ y

Directions: Say the name of each picture. Print the capital and small letters for its beginning sound.

Directions: Say the name of each picture. Print the letter for its beginning sound.

___ie	___ig	___un	___all
___in	___ap	___ire	___ive
___am	___et	___ug	___og

Directions: Say the name of each picture. Print the letter for its ending sound. Color all the pictures.

to	we	do	be
pai	cu	su	bu
ha	lea	bo	dru

Directions: Say the name of each picture. Print the small letter for its ending sound. Color the pictures.

Directions: Say the name of each picture. If you hear the consonant beside the picture at the beginning, circle the consonant at the left. If you hear it at the end, circle the consonant at the right.

s	(dress)	s	d	(rose)	d	g	(dog)	g
h	(house)	h	f	(fish)	f	p	(top)	p
r	(star)	r	c	(cup)	c	l	(leaf)	l
y	(yarn)	y	t	(basket)	t	j	(jeep)	j
w	(wig)	w	b	(boat)	b	n	(moon)	n
x	(6)	x	m	(mop)	m	k	(kite)	k

Directions: Say the name of each picture. Print the letter for its beginning sound. Then print the letter for its ending sound to complete the name of the picture.

_ e _

_ o _

_ u _

_ o _

_ a _

_ i _

_ e _

_ u _

_ o _

_ i _

_ a _

_ e _

LESSON 5: Beginning and final consonants

_____

- -

_____

Directions: Say the name of each picture. Print the letter for the sound you hear in the middle of the word. The first one is done for you.

d

Directions: Say the name of each picture. Print the middle letter in the space to complete its name. Read the sentences.

dra ___ on

ba ___ y

ra ___ io

spi ___ er

ti ___ er

pea ___ ut

7 se ___ en

ca ___ el

Ted will get his wa ___ on.

Color the wa ___ on red.

I can see the ca ___ in.

Color the ca ___ in brown.

Jill has six coo ___ ies.

Color the coo ___ ies brown.

See the tu ___ ip in the vase.

Color the tu ___ ip yellow.

I need the bo ___ es.

Color the bo ___ es blue.

Jan got a le ___ on.

Color the le ___ on yellow.

Directions: Say the name of each picture. Print the missing letters to complete the picture name. Read the sentences.

Ted has a wa_____on.

Color the wa_____on red.

The _____un is hot.

Color the _____un yellow.

Sand is in the pai_____.

Color the pai_____ green.

Play the ra_____io.

Color the ra_____io red.

Pam takes a _____us ride.

Color the _____us yellow.

A bug is on the lea_____.

Color the lea_____ green.

A deer is at the ca_____in.

Color the ca_____in red.

Ken will spin the _____op.

Color the _____op yellow.

Directions: Say the name of each picture. In the spaces below each picture, print the letters for the beginning, middle, and ending sounds.

LESSON 7: Beginning, medial, and final consonants

Directions: Circle the name of each picture.

⌒ If a word or syllable has only one vowel and it comes at the beginning or between two consonants, the vowel usually stands for a short sound.

hat	ham	bag	hat	camp	lad
hand	had	bat	bad	lap	lamp

sad	back	cat	cap	tam	jam
bag	bat	cab	can	Jan	Sam

wax	ax	mat	man	tag	tan
am	at	fan	tan	tap	tack

and	an	cat	can	mad	man
at	ant	cab	cap	map	mat

Directions: Read each list of words. Circle the word that does not rhyme. Draw its picture.

cat		Max		cap	
fan		tax		tap	
hat		bag		map	
mat		wax		cab	
sack		bag		sand	
hand		rag		land	
back		cap		pan	
tack		tag		band	
ham		sad		quack	
fan		bat		cat	
ran		bad		sack	
can		had		back	
hand		pan		sat	
land		fan		ax	
lamp		Dan		pat	
sand		hat		fat	

Directions: Say the name of each picture, and print its name below it. Then print a word that rhymes with it. Do what the sentences tell you to do.

Color the bag red.
Color the fan green.

Color the cap red.
Color the ax blue.

Color the cat black.
Color the tack yellow.

Color the lamp green and black.
Color the jam red and blue.

LESSON 9: Short vowel A   **17**

Directions: Circle the word that completes each sentence. Print it on the line. Read the sentence to be sure it makes sense.

1. The _____ at bat had a cap.   band   man   sack

2. Ann had a pal at the _____ .   cat   lamp   camp

3. Pam has a tan _____ .   ran   van   jam

4. Hand the bag of _____ to the man.   sand   hand   band

5. An _____ ran past the sack.   ant   an   at

6. _____ the ham and jam to Nat.   Pat   Bass   Pass

7. Dad had a can of _____ .   rap   has   gas

8. Dan swam back to _____ .   land   band   fast

9. At _____ I ran as fast as Mac.   sat   last   tack

10. Val and Pat _____ bags at camp.   pan   back   pack

11. Babs sat on a _____ in the sand.   fat   mat   map

12. Sam, hand Sal the _____ .   lamp   van   fast

Directions: Circle the name of each picture.

⬡ If a word or syllable has only one vowel and it comes at the beginning or between two consonants, the vowel usually stands for a short sound.

silk milk mill bill	mitt bit fit mill	lid hid lip tip
tips lips dips dill	big pig fig pit	Bit Bib Bill Hill
Tin Fill Jill Jim	bill bit hit bib	ink wink sink pink
hill bill sill mltt	mix six fix blt	win tin will pin

Directions: Say the words in each ball. Use the same color to color the parts of each ball with rhyming words.

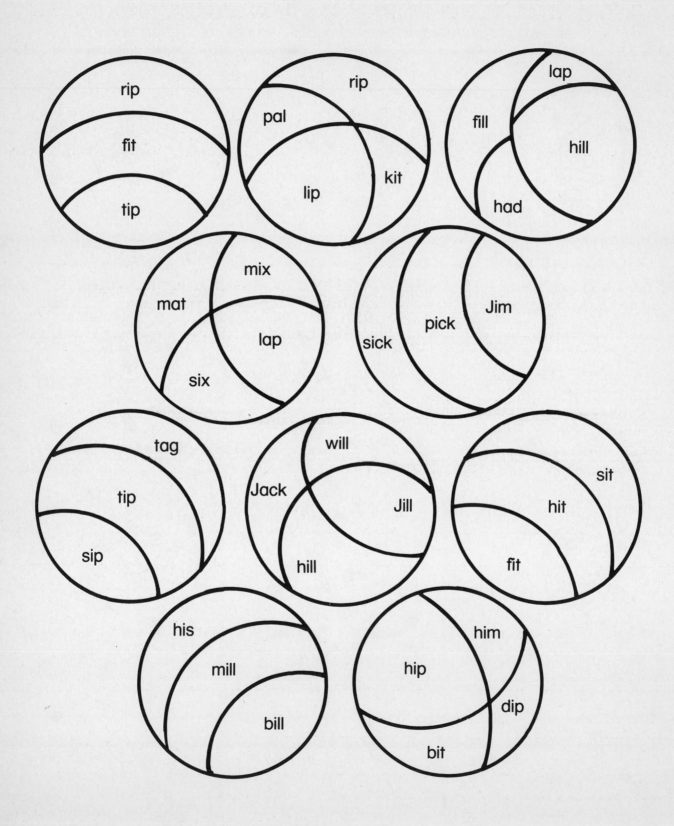

_____

- - - - - - - - - - - - - - - - - -

Directions: Say the name of each picture, and print its name below it. Then print a word that rhymes with it.

- - - - - - - - - - - - - - - - - -

Directions: Read each riddle. Circle the correct answer in the word list. Print it on the line. The first one is done for you.

It can swim. What is it?	It fits on a pot. What is it?	A dog can do this. What is it?

fish

| fist | (fish) | lip | lit | dish | dim |
| fix | fit | lid | list | did | dig |

We can do this to Mom. What is it?	Lunch goes on it. What is it?	We use them to speak. What are they?

| kiss | kin | dill | dish | licks | lists |
| king | kit | dig | dip | lips | lifts |

We skate on it. What is it?	Baby needs this. What is it?	We play with it. What is it?

| rip | rid | bib | bid | mint | mitt |
| rig | rink | bill | bit | mill | mix |

Jack and Jill ran up it. What is it?	It has a funny tail. What is it?	We can fill it. What is it?

| hit | hip | pin | pig | sill | sit |
| hill | him | pill | pit | sip | sink |

Directions: Read the words that are part of a sentence that is started for you. Finish the sentence using all the words in the box at the right.

1. Did Tim _____ ?

the
bag
fill

2. Jim hid with the _____ .

cat
big
fat

3. Ann and Kim will _____ .

sit
Bill
with

4. The cat will _____ .

the
rip
sack

5. The lid will fit _____ .

pan
big
the

6. Sid and I can _____ .

six
quit
at

7. I will ask Jill to _____ .

the
bat
fix

8. Pam and Dad can _____ .

the
hit
ball

9. Did the cat _____ ?

bag
the
tip

Directions: Circle the word that will complete each sentence, and print it on the line. Read the sentence to be sure it makes sense.

1. Dan had a _____ for Rick.   him   gift   lift

2. A pan of milk is in the _____ .   sink   rink   sank

3. The cat hid in a _____ hat.   big   bag   bat

4. Ann will _____ the lamp.   band   mix   fix

5. Kim had a sip of _____ .   mile   milk   wick

6. I will dig and dig in the _____ .   mad   hand   sand

7. The man will sit on the _____ .   hill   fill   tan

8. Lin and Dad _____ in the cab.   sick   fat   sat

9. The tin pan had a big _____ .   limp   lid   ran

10. Nick's mitt will fit in the _____ . hill   miss   bag

11. Vic hid the _____ in the sand.   bat   bit   big

12. The ball hit the big _____ .   sat   van   wag

Directions: Circle the name of each picture. In the box, print the letter that stands for the vowel sound you hear in the word you circled.

○ If a word or syllable has only one vowel and it comes at the beginning or between two consonants, the vowel usually stands for a short sound.

cap cup	gas gull	Dick duck
_____	_____	_____
kit	gum	Dad
_____	_____	_____
can cup	jug jam	tug tip
_____	_____	_____
cap	just	bug
_____	_____	_____
but nuts	calf cut	sack six
_____	_____	_____
nap	cuff	sick
_____	_____	_____
ask ax	as bun	sun sum
_____	_____	_____
is	bus	dim
_____	_____	_____

Directions: Read the words in the box above the pictures, and find the picture that goes with each word. Then print the name of each picture in the space below it.

bud	cup	rug	bus	bug	sun
gum	pup	cuff	tub	jug	duck

_____
_ _ _ _ _ _ _ _ _ _ _ _ _ _
_____

Directions: Circle the correct answer in the word list, and print it on the line.

I am full of milk.	I can say, "Yip, yip."	You can eat me.
What am I?	What am I ?	What am I?
_____	_____	_____
_ _ _ _ _ _	_ _ _ _ _ _	_ _ _ _ _ _
_____	_____	_____
up cut	cup up	cut but
cup cuff	pup cut	fun nut

I hid in the jug.	A hot dog fills me up.	This is fun to do.
What am I?	What am I ?	What is it?
_____	_____	_____
_ _ _ _ _ _	_ _ _ _ _ _	_ _ _ _ _ _
_____	_____	_____
bus tub	dug bun	just lump
sun bug	fun run	muff Jump

This is quick to do.	You can ride in me.	You can see me.
What is it?	What am I ?	What am I?
_____	_____	_____
_ _ _ _ _ _	_ _ _ _ _ _	_ _ _ _ _ _
_____	_____	_____
fun run	bud bug	sun but
bun cup	bus us	run fun

I say, "Quack, quack."	We can do this to Dad.	A pig digs in this.
What am I?	What is it?	What is it?
_____	_____	_____
_ _ _ _ _ _	_ _ _ _ _ _	_ _ _ _ _ _
_____	_____	_____
tuck luck	up lump	just but
pup duck	sun hug	mud must

Directions: Circle the word that will complete each sentence, and print it on the line. Read the sentence to be sure it makes sense.

1. A duck cannot _____ fast.

rug
run
bat
cup

2. Ann's _____ can jump up to the tub.

pup
bus
cup
rug

3. We had a _____ full of milk.

but
cut
jug
nuts

4. Gus and Kim _____ in the mud.

cub
bus
rug
dug

5. Pam and I will sit in the _____ .

bun
sun
gum
dug

6. Did you see the yellow bug in the _____ ?

just
lug
dust
must

7. Russ and Judd run and _____ at the camp.

jump
mumps
bump
lump

8. The cub had _____ with the ball.

fun
tub
sun
rug

9. The pup _____ and pulls on the cuff.

tubs
cups
tugs
rugs

_____

- - - - - - - - - - - - - - - - -

_____
_____

Directions: Make new words by changing the vowels. Print the new words on the lines. The first one is started for you.

	i	u
fan	fin	
bad		
ham		
hat		
as		
bag		
rag		

Directions: Have fun with these questions. Circle the correct answer.

1. Can a black pup run with Max?   Yes   No

2. Is a big cup a little nut?   Yes   No

3. Is the sun black?   Yes   No

4. Can a cat run fast?   Yes   No

5. Can a big pig sing for you?   Yes   No

6. Can we nap in a tan van?   Yes   No

7. Can a man run up a hill?   Yes   No

8. Is a green rug red?   Yes   No

9. Is Ann a big map?   Yes   No

10. Can you sit on a bus?   Yes   No

11. Can a little cup run fast and jump?   Yes   No

12. Will a cat hug a rat?   Yes   No

13. Can you fill a pan with milk?   Yes   No

14. Can a doll jump on the bus?   Yes   No

15. Can a pig go as fast as a cab?   Yes   No

16. Can you rub your hands?   Yes   No

17. Is a sad cat happy?   Yes   No

18. Can a bus be big?   Yes   No

19. Can a bug sit in the mud?   Yes   No

20. Can a hug nap on a rug?   Yes   No

Directions: Read the words in the list above the pictures, and find the picture that goes with each word. Then print the name of each picture in the space below it.

⬡ If a word or syllable has only one vowel and it comes at the beginning or between two consonants, the vowel usually stands for a short sound.

| top | mop | pot | box | Tom | sock |
| cot | doll | fox | lock | rock | rod |

Directions: Circle the name of each picture.

fix
cob
fox
six

pot
top
tap
pit

bill
sill
dill
doll

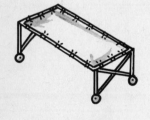
cot
dot
job
cut

dug
dog
dig
pot

rob
rid
rap
rod

pig
pop
pup
pat

lag
log
bug
lot

luck
lock
lick
lack

Directions: Color the circle in front of the sentence that tells about each picture. Draw a box around each short **O** word in the sentences.

○ The fox is not on the log.

○ The fox is in the log.

○ The fox is on the log.

○ The fox is under the log.

○ Bob lost his socks.

○ Bob sat on a big rock.

○ Bob is on the big log.

○ Bob has a big rock in his hand.

○ The dog ran to the box.

○ The mop is not in the box.

○ I will hop, hop, hop to the log.

○ See the doll in the box.

○ I got the doll on the cot.

○ Jill can see the big top.

○ The big top is on the mop.

○ The red top is in Bob's hand.

○ Hot milk is in a pot.

○ The big doll is in the box.

○ The milk in the cup is hot.

○ The big red top is his.

Directions: Circle the name of each picture.

six fix	bun hit	doll bill	tan fan
sit sun	box fox	dot dog	fun fin
cup cap	mat cot	sick sock	rock luck
kit can	mop pop	son sack	lock sock
fix fox	pin top	tick rack	pot dug
box fun	pot tip	tuck rock	dog log

Directions: Print the name of each picture in the space below it.

Directions: Find the word in the list at the right that will complete each sentence. Then print the word on the line. Read each sentence to be sure it makes sense.

1. Ron is fond of his pet _____ .   Jack

2. I see a bug with dots on _____ back.   bus

3. Jan will ride in the yellow _____ .   box

4. Rick and _____ will fill the bag with nuts.   duck

5. I will _____ up to the pond.   its

6. Mom can toss the ring into the _____ .   jog

---

1. Jim and Dan got a _____ tan.   full

2. Dot has a box _____ of pins.   mitt

3. Tom sat on a big _____ .   rock

4. I will sip the _____ milk.   sun

5. Pam and Jill put the cans in a _____ .   hot

6. Will the _____ fit on his hand?   sack

_____

- -

_____

Directions: Print the name of each picture on the line with the same numeral as the picture.

○ If a word or syllable has only one vowel and it comes at the beginning or between two consonants, the vowel usually stands for a short sound.

1. _____

2. _____

3. _____

4. _____

5. _____

6. _____

7. _____

8. _____

9. _____

10. _____

11. _____

12. _____

1

2

3

4

5

6

7

8

9

10

11

12

LESSON 19: Short vowel E   **37**

Directions: First, read the sentences and do what they tell you to do. Then print the name of each picture on the line next to it.

1. Find the bed.

   Color it red and blue.

2. Find the hen.

   Color it yellow.

3. Find the nest.

   Color three eggs red and

   three eggs blue.

4. See the tent.

   Color it yellow.

5. See the belt.

   Color it green.

6. Find the vest.

   Color it red and black.

Directions: Circle the word that will complete each sentence, and print it on the line. Read the sentence to be sure it makes sense.

1. Red Hen sat on the _____ .   nest   best   bet

2. Jen will lend Ted the green _____ .   rest   sled   vet

3. Ken's blue jet _____ off the box.   bet   fell   fill

4. Lin will run and _____ the bat.   get   met   bad

5. The hen did not _____ at Jeff.   peck   pen   ten

6. I sat at Meg's _____ .   dust   desk   dill

7. The _____ has blue ink in it.   pen   pin   pill

8. Tell Ed to _____ Mom.   held   vest   help

9. Jill has a _____ truck full of rocks.   red   fed   led

10. He has a _____ and a cap in the box.   bet   let   belt

11. Sis gets the tent on the _____ .   help   left   let

12. The pup can be a big _____ .   best   peg   pest

Directions: Print the name of each picture on the line.

_____	_____	_____	_____	_____

Directions: Read each sentence. Then print **yes** or **no** on the line at the right.

1. You can nap in a bed.   _____

2. I can get ten eggs for the box.   _____

3. A cat has six legs.   _____

4. A big bus can jump up and down.   _____

5. Mom can help get a can of gas.   _____

6. You can go fast in a jet.   _____

7. An ant is as big as an ox.   _____

8. Six is less than ten.   _____

9. You can sit in a tent.   _____

_____

- -

Directions: Read each sentence that is started for you. Then read the word on the right. Change the vowel in the word to make a new word that will complete the sentence. Print the word on the line. The first one is done for you.

1. Bev left the quilt on the ___bed___ .   bad

2. Yes, the sun will _____ in the west.   sat

3. The vet will help the _____ .   pop

4. The cat _____ up the milk in the pan.   lips

5. Pat will help us _____ the rock.   left

6. The cub got _____ in the fog.   last

1. Can Max lift the _____ box off the bus?   bag

2. Lock the box and set it on the _____ .   disk

3. Miss Nell _____ the pen on the desk.   lift

4. Did the dog run to Bob and _____ his hand?   lack

5. A gust of wind _____ the tent.   hat

6. Deb and I play catch with the _____ .   bell.

LESSON 21: Reviewing short vowels A, I, U, O, E   **41**

Directions: Print the name of each picture on the line.

_____   _____   _____   _____

Directions: Change the vowel to make a new word.

tug   _____   rip   _____   tab   _____

fox   _____   fad   _____   hunt   _____

rust   _____   sand   _____   tint   _____

Directions: Find the word that will complete each sentence. Print it on the line.

1. Hand Judd his _____ and socks.   cub

2. Sam fell in the _____ and got wet.   lit

3. At dusk Mom _____ the lamp on the desk.   belt

4. You may not pet the _____ .   bat

5. Dot is at _____ next.   pond

Directions: Read each sentence. Find the missing word, and print it on the line.

○ If a one-part word or syllable has two vowels, the first vowel usually stands for a long sound, and the second is silent.

cave

pail

rake

1. Nate _____ a nut cake for Mom.   mail

2. You will be _____ if you wait for me.   pain

3. Kate _____ late to the game.   came

4. Dave had a bad _____ in his leg.   made

5. Ted can take the _____ from the box.   late

1. Jane _____ the man for the jug of milk.   lake

2. It is safe to wade in the _____ .   train

3. The _____ of the ape is Jake.   paid

4. Tom gave a red _____ with buds to Mom.   vase

5. Can you _____ the dog to do a trick?   name

Directions: Circle the word that belongs in each sentence. Print it on the line.

1. We got tape at the _____ .   sap   sale   same

2. Jane may _____ in the lake.   wade   way   with

3. Dave gave Kay the big red _____ .   pay   fail   pail

4. Did you see the cubs in the _____ ?   cape   cave   came

5. Will you _____ to Jake and Ray?   sat   save   wave

6. Jay will bake Kate a _____ .   cake   case   fake

Directions: Circle each long **A** word.

tap	tape	cap	cape	at	ate
mail	mat	rain	gate	hay	ham

Directions: Print the name of each picture on the line. Use the words in the list above.

_____

_____

Directions: Circle the name of each picture.

fin fire	pig pile	bike big	bib bite

Directions: Circle the word that belongs in each sentence. Print it on the line.

I will pay a _____ for it.

dime   dim   dill

Jill will _____ the ball.

hate   hill   hit

He will ride his _____ .

big   bike   like

Take the _____ to Jake.

lie   tie   like

A bug has _____ legs.

sick   hide   six

Lil has a big red _____ .

kit   time   kite

Jane will bake a _____ .

pipe   pie   pill

I _____ to dive.

life   like   lick

Mike sees a bee _____ .

fit   fine   hive

Russ can tell _____ .

time   tire   tip

Directions: Circle the word that belongs in each sentence. Print it on the line.

_____
_ _ _ _ _ _ _ _

1. Take your _____ to the lake.   big   bike   bite

_____
_ _ _ _ _ _ _ _

2. Mike will tie a tail to his _____ .   kite   kit   hide

_____
_ _ _ _ _ _ _ _

3. Kim likes to _____ the bus.   hid   rid   ride

_____
_ _ _ _ _ _ _ _

4. Bill cannot _____ a mile.   bake   hike   hide

_____
_ _ _ _ _ _ _ _

5. Val gave us a _____ melon.   ripe   ride   rip

_____
_ _ _ _ _ _ _ _

6. Did the dog save the man's _____ ?   lift   life   like

_____
_ _ _ _ _ _ _ _

7. Liz had a big _____ of pie.   pine   five   bite

Directions: Circle each long **I** word

dim	dime	pin	pine	rid	ride
mine	tie	sit	kite	nine	fire

Directions: Print the name of each picture. Use the words from the list above.

_ _ _ _ _ _ _ _ _ | _ _ _ _ _ _ _ _ _ | _ _ _ _ _ _ _ _ _ | _ _ _ _ _ _ _ _ _

Directions: Read each sentence. Find the correct word in the list at the right, and print it on the line.

1. We did it in a game. _____ rain   ran   man

2. A dog has it. _____ tail   pail   pat

3. We did it to Pat's cake. _____ at   late   ate

4. Jane has a can for it. _____ pat   pain   paint

5. A dog can do this. _____ wag   way   rag

6. We like to see this. _____ bake   mile   lake

7. A can has this. _____ did   died   lid

8. We like to eat it. _____ bit   pie   pat

9. We can ride it. _____ bill   bat   bike

10. Dave can put it on. _____ tip   tie   time

11. We can save this. _____ like   dime   dip

12. A wet day has this. _____ rain   rate   ran

Directions: Say the words on the balloons. If a word has the long sound of **A**, print it below Kay's name. If a word has the long sound of **I**, print it below Mike's name.

Kay

_____

_____

_____

_____

_____

Mike

_____

_____

_____

_____

_____

Directions: Read each sentence. Circle the answer at the right. Then circle the long **U** word in each sentence. Print the long **U** words on the lines below.

1. A red vase is blue.   Yes   No
2. A mule can kick.   Yes   No
3. A flute is a drum.   Yes   No
4. A cube can play with a bat.   Yes   No
5. A mule has nine tails.   Yes   No
6. The five ducks are cute.   Yes   No
7. Sue can sit in the sun.   Yes   No
8. A cube has six sides.   Yes   No
9. You can eat a suit.   Yes   No
10. A tube is a top that can sing.   Yes   No
11. We can use the tire.   Yes   No
12. We can sing a tune.   Yes   No

1. _____
2. _____
3. _____
4. _____

5. _____
6. _____
7. _____
8. _____

9. _____
10. _____
11. _____
12. _____

Directions: Read the words in the list at the left. Print the short **U** words on the short **U** ladder. Print the long **U** words on the long **U** ladder.

◯ If a one-part word or syllable has two vowels, the first vowel usually stands for a long sound, and the second is silent.

Short **U**	Long **U**

cute

must

bug

duck

jump

suit

tune

bump

tube

dug

cube

mule

nut

fuse

use

bud

rule

cuff

hum

rude

Directions: Read each word below. If the word is a long vowel word, circle **long**. If the word is a short vowel word, circle **short**.

late	**long** **short**	June	**long** **short**	mule	**long** **short**
man	**long** **short**	milk	**long** **short**	rake	**long** **short**
rain	**long** **short**	pick	**long** **short**	six	**long** **short**
use	**long** **short**	cute	**long** **short**	cap	**long** **short**
bat	**long** **short**	time	**long** **short**	fun	**long** **short**
suit	**long** **short**	lick	**long** **short**	us	**long** **short**
map	**long** **short**	wide	**long** **short**	gate	**long** **short**
tame	**long** **short**	pie	**long** **short**	tune	**long** **short**
lap	**long** **short**	ate	**long** **short**	fill	**long** **short**
up	**long** **short**	fire	**long** **short**	make	**long** **short**
tube	**long** **short**	cut	**long** **short**	ride	**long** **short**
bake	**long** **short**	wipe	**long** **short**	nut	**long** **short**

Directions: Read each sentence that is started for you. Circle the word that will complete the sentence. Print the word on the line.

1. I paid a _____ for the nuts.   dim   dime   cat

2. Sue has _____ blue cups.   fix   fan   six

3. Dad gave Jim a red _____ .   sun   tie   sit

4. The _____ melt fast in the pop.   came   cubs   cubes

5. May I use June's _____ of paste?   tub   tube   tune

6. It is _____ to get the mule.   tune   tip   time

7. We _____ milk and pie.   had   hid   suit

8. We ran fast side by _____ .   side   sum   wide

9. Mom will _____ us to the game.   like   tack   take

10. Mike likes to bake a _____ .   pin   pie   tie

11. Tim had on a _____ suit.   bud   rule   blue

12. Gail will _____ at the gate.   day   pay   pail

Directions: Circle each long **O** word in the list.

○ If a one-part word or syllable has two vowels, the first vowel usually stands for a long sound, and the second is silent.

rod	road	rode	cot	coat	got	goat
hope	hop	robe	rob	row	cost	coast

Directions: Read each sentence that is started for you. Find the word in the list on the right that will complete each sentence. Print the word on the line.

1. You may go home with _____.   mow

2. See the big _____ on the lake.   coat

3. Joan had a red hat and _____ .   Joan

4. Moe has a _____ for a pet.   rope

5. The dog dug a _____ for his bone.   row

6. We _____ the bus to the big cave.   note

7. Joe sent a _____ to his pal.   rode

8. Joan and Jay like to jump _____ .   boat

9. Cole has time to _____ the grass.   goat

10. It is fun to _____ the boat.   hole

Directions: Circle the name of each picture.

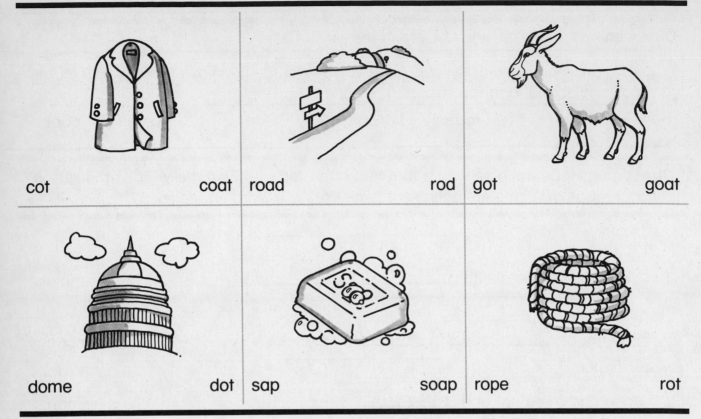

cot coat	road rod	got goat
dome dot	sap soap	rope rot

Directions: Read each sentence that is started for you. The word that belongs in each sentence rhymes with the one that follows the sentence. Print it on the line.

_____
_ _ _ _ _ _ _ _ _ _ _

1. I _____ it will not rain for the game.   rope

_____
_ _ _ _ _ _ _ _ _ _ _

2. Joan has a vase for the pink _____ .   nose

_____
_ _ _ _ _ _ _ _ _ _ _

3. Joe will toss a bone to his _____ .   fog

_____
_ _ _ _ _ _ _ _ _ _ _

4. Sue ran up the _____ to see Pam.   toad

_____
_ _ _ _ _ _ _ _ _ _ _

5. Tie a big _____ on the gift.   row

_____

- -

_____

Directions: Read the words in the first box. Use them to find the name of each picture and print it on the line.

mail	dive
bake	five
soap	hope
tube	kite
cube	toad

_____   _____

- - - - - - - - - - - - - -   - - - - - - - - - - - - - -

_____   _____

_____   _____   _____

- - - - - - - - -   - - - - - - - - -   - - - - - - - - -

_____   _____   _____

Directions: Find the word in the list at the right that belongs in each sentence, and print it on the line.

_____

- - - - - - - - -

1. Kate can jump _____ with Fay.   hike

- - - - - - - - -

2. The boys sat on a rock at the _____ .   cake

- - - - - - - - -

3. Dale will bake a date _____ .   rope

- - - - - - - - -

4. Kay hit the ball with the _____ .   lake

- - - - - - - - -

5. James put on his blue _____ .   suit

- - - - - - - - -

6. It is fun to take a _____ .   bat

Directions: Read the sentence that is started for you. Circle the word that belongs in the sentence, and print it on the line.

1. Jane and Jack _____ a date cake.   mad   made

2. Jack had a big _____ of the cake.   bit   bite

3. Mom will take _____ to camp.   us   use

4. I lost a _____ on the way home.   dime   dim

5. Kay ran with the big blue _____ .   kite   kit

6. Ask Joan to _____ the rose on my coat.   pine   pin

7. You may _____ the pen on my desk.   use   us

8. Miss Dell sent a _____ to Mom.   not   note

9. Did you _____ the rope and the hoe?   hid   hide

10. Duke will soak in a _____ of suds.   tub   tube

11. I _____ I win the prize.   hope   hop

12. Can you hand me a _____ in a cup?   cube   cub

_____

Directions: Circle the name of the picture.

set
seal
seed

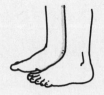

feel
fell
feet

seat
sat
soap

heel
hill
heat

beets
beds
beads

jet
jeep
Jean

Directions: Read the sentences that are started for you. Find the word that belongs in the sentence, and print it on the line.

1. Pete will feed _____ to his dog.
   met   meat   neat

2. Ken will keep the bag of _____ for his meal.
   beans   beads   bed

3. Did you see the bees _____ the hive near the road?
   lean   leaf   leave

4. Dean and Eve will meet me next _____ to go on a picnic.
   wet   weed   week

5. Jean and Lee made the _____ .
   teen   team   ten

Directions: Read each sentence. Draw a ring around the long **E** word in each sentence, and print it on the line.

1. Pat fed the seal.

    _____

2. I can see a tent by the boat.

    _____

3. The next day Ted ate a big meal.

    _____

4. Jean has a big rose on her hat.

    _____

5. Jill rode fast in the jeep.

    _____

6. I will keep the cake for Ben.

    _____

7. The big dog is a gift for Eve.

    _____

8. Do you feel well?

    _____

9. Fran cut the red beets for a salad.

    _____

10. Dad will roast the meat in a pan with a lid.

    _____

11. Jen can row the boat to the reef.

    _____

12. Dave likes to read in bed.

    _____

Directions: Print the letter on the line that stands for the vowel sound you hear in the name of the picture. Then find a picture for each sound in the list. Print the number of each sound in the correct circle. The first one is done for you.

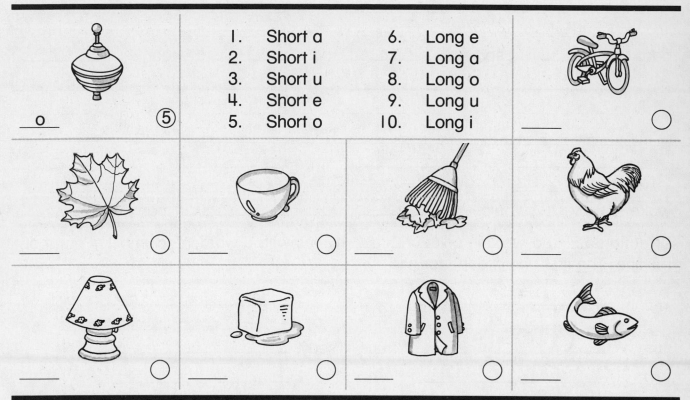

o ⑤	1. Short a 6. Long e 2. Short i 7. Long a 3. Short u 8. Long o 4. Short e 9. Long u 5. Short o 10. Long i		___ ○
___ ○	___ ○	___ ○	___ ○
___ ○	___ ○	___ ○	___ ○

Directions: Complete the rhyming words.

hat   mat   sat   gate   ___ d

went   d___   r___   like   b___   h___

fun   r___   b___   goat   c___   b___

seed   n___   w___   rip   z___   t___

June   d___   t___   pop   m___   h___

LESSON 30: Reviewing long and short vowels and rhyming words   **59**

Directions: Change the first vowel in each word to make a new word, and print it.

man _____ Kate _____ bake _____ had _____

boat _____ sod _____ red _____ oar _____

hop _____ ran _____ cone _____ wide _____

wake _____ nip _____ tame _____ map _____

Directions: Find a word in column 2 that rhymes with a word in column 1. Print it on the line. The first one is done for you.

①		②		①		②
time	dime	tube		seat		tin
cube		cub		fin		road
big		cape		hope		cob
rub		dime		bet		rope
need		hat		rob		late
tape		feed		ate		get
bat		dig		toad		heat

Directions: Say the name of each picture. Color the box with the word **short** if the vowel sound is short. Color the box with **long** if it is long. Then print the letter that stands for the vowel sound you hear.

short	long		short	long		short	long		short	long	

short	long		short	long		short	long		short	long	

short	long		short	long		short	long		short	long	

short	long		short	long		short	long		short	long	

Directions: Read each sentence that is started for you. Circle the word that belongs in the sentence, and print it on the line.

1. Mack left his _____ on the rack.   heat   hat   hit

2. Pete sat in a _____ of suds.   tub   rub   cub

3. The cub will not _____ you.   bit   bite   kite

4. Jean's dog is _____ .   rut   cube   cute

5. Dad has the eggs in a _____ .   fox   sail   box

6. Did Tom use the blue _____ ?   load   hole   bowl

7. Dot will sail the _____ on the lake.   cot   boat   coat

8. Dan can plant _____ in the pot.   seeds   deeds   seals

9. I see a lot of _____ on the desk.   sail   pail   mail

10. The dog ate the _____ in the pan.   met   meat   seat

11. Bev will help clean up the _____ .   must   mean   mess

12. Rags had _____ pups.   six   size   sit

Directions: Put two words together to make a new word, and print it on the line.

| pea | weed | | meal | oat |
| sea | nut | | my | self |

_____

_____

| cup | rain | | be | rail |
| coat | cake | | road | may |

_____

_____

| base | class | | day | dog |
| mate | ball | | dream | bull |

_____

_____

Directions: Look at the picture and the words below it. Put the two words together to make a compound word. Print the compound word to finish the sentence. The first one is done for you.

tea + pot

A pot for tea is a __teapot__.

mail + box

A box for mail is a _____.

rain + coat

A coat for rain is a _____.

bath + tub

A tub for a bath is a _____.

pan + cake

A cake in a pan is a _____.

sail + boat

A boat with a sail is a _____.

row + boat

A boat you row is a _____.

Directions: Say the name of the picture. Circle each vowel you hear in the picture name. Print the number of word parts, or syllables, you hear in the picture name. The first ones are done for you.

Many words are made of small parts called syllables.

Each syllable has one vowel sound.

c(a)t = 1 syllable   k(i)t t(e)n = 2 syllables

b(a)s k(e)t   mittens   steps

pencil   tent   puppet

trunk   rabbit   tulip

Directions: Look at the picture that goes with each sentence. Find the picture name in the list at the top. Print the word in the sentence. Read the story you make.

| basket | kitten | baby |
| pillow | button | seven |

Randy got a _____ named Samson.

Samson was _____ weeks old.

He had a nose like a _____ .

Randy put Samson in a _____ .

He gave Samson a _____ .

Samson was like a _____ .

Directions: Say the name of each picture. If the name has the soft sound **C** can stand for, color the picture orange. If it has the hard sound, color it blue.

○ When **c** is followed by **e**, **i**, or **y**, it usually stands for a soft sound.

fence	cap	clock
cup	pencil	cake
mice	candle	celery
coat	face	rice

Directions: Read each sentence that is started for you. Find the word that belongs in the sentence, and print it on the line.

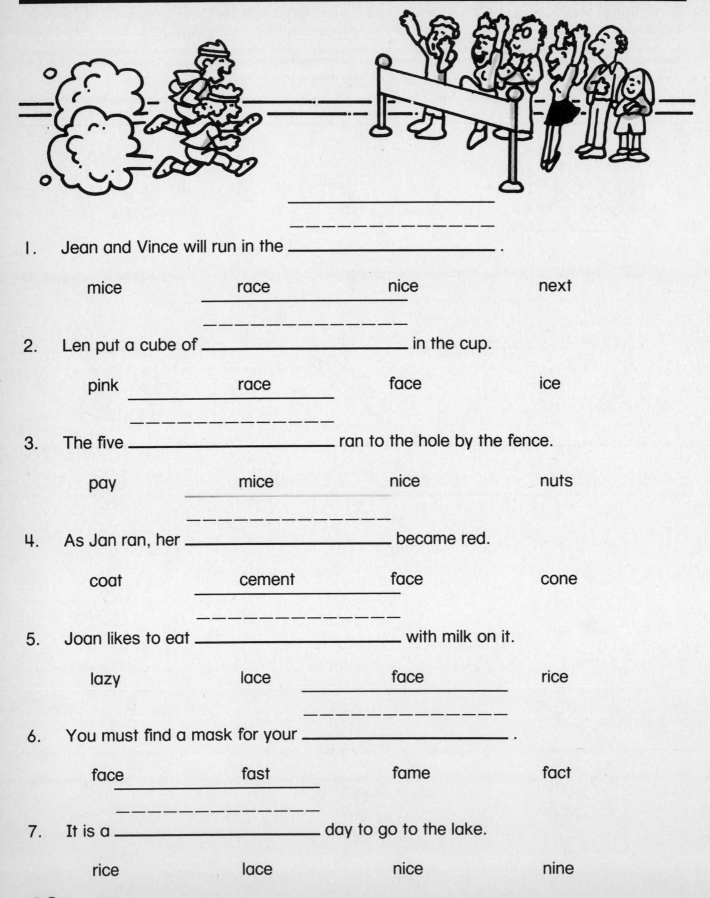

1. Jean and Vince will run in the _____ .

   mice　　　　　　race　　　　　　nice　　　　　　next

2. Len put a cube of _____ in the cup.

   pink　　　　　　race　　　　　　face　　　　　　ice

3. The five _____ ran to the hole by the fence.

   pay　　　　　　mice　　　　　　nice　　　　　　nuts

4. As Jan ran, her _____ became red.

   coat　　　　　　cement　　　　　face　　　　　　cone

5. Joan likes to eat _____ with milk on it.

   lazy　　　　　　lace　　　　　　face　　　　　　rice

6. You must find a mask for your _____ .

   face　　　　　　fast　　　　　　fame　　　　　　fact

7. It is a _____ day to go to the lake.

   rice　　　　　　lace　　　　　　nice　　　　　　nine

Directions: Say the name of each picture. If the name has the soft sound of **G**, color the picture orange. If it has the hard sound of **G**, color the picture green.

⬡ When **g** is followed by **e, i,** or **y,** it usually stands for a soft sound.

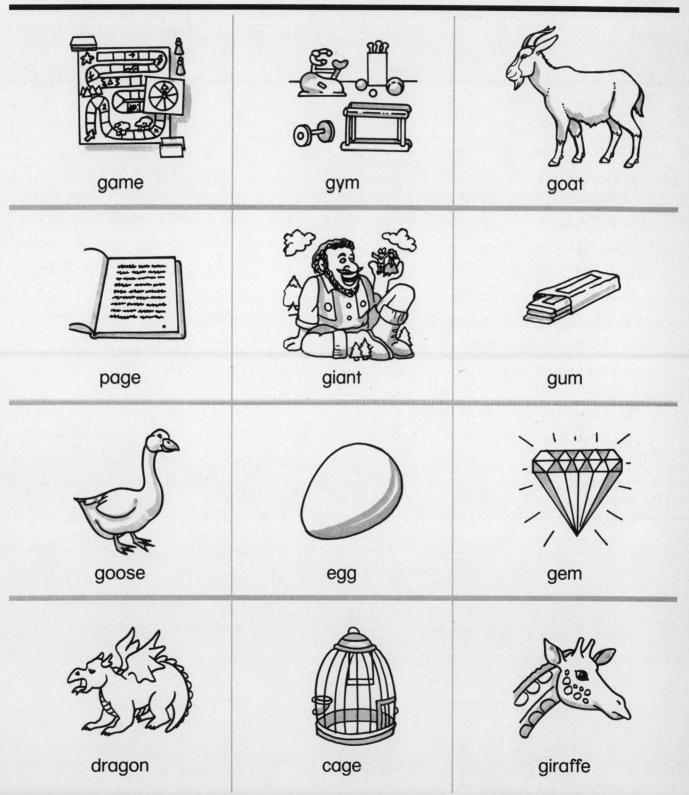

game	gym	goat
page	giant	gum
goose	egg	gem
dragon	cage	giraffe

Directions: The letter **G** has two sounds—hard or soft. Print each word you see at the top of the page on a line in the correct column.

○ When **g** is followed by **e**, **i**, or **y**, it usually stands for a soft sound.

gem	goes	dog	cage	gum	good
gave	age	stage	wag	wage	Gene
gym	goat	giant	egg	game	page

Soft **g** words

_____
_____
_____
_____
_____
_____
_____
_____
_____
_____
_____

Hard **g** words

_____
_____
_____
_____
_____
_____
_____
_____
_____
_____
_____

Directions: Draw a blue line under each word in the list that has the hard sound of **C** or **G**. Print each word that has the soft sound of **C** or **G** in a bubble.

price

mice

goat

age

wage

games

huge

cent

gem

ice

gym

cake

cell

lunge

race

rice

gas

cone

face

giant

LESSON 36: Hard and soft C and G

71

Directions: Print S if the word has the soft sound of **C** or **G**; print H if the word has the hard sound of **C** or **G**.

nice _____   cuff _____   ice _____   cabin _____   lunge _____

camel _____   game _____   race _____   gull _____   age _____

came _____   coast _____   cake _____   coat _____   pencil _____

gym _____   cent _____   giant _____   gate _____   ridge _____

care _____   goes _____   recess _____   Vince _____   page _____

mice _____   rice _____   gem _____   Gail _____   gum _____

Directions: Draw a red box around each soft **G** word. Draw a blue circle around each soft **C** word.

1. Gail gave Vince a cage for his pet.

2. After the game they held a dance in the gym.

3. A fence ran along the ridge of the hill.

4. Gary will not budge from his seat near the TV.

5. Cindy saw the new bridge in the city.

6. The giant wildcat is at the edge of the cave.

7. A pack of gum will cost you ten cents.

8. The desk lamp casts a red dot on the yellow ceiling.

_____

_____

Directions: Say the name of each picture. Print the blend that stands for the sound you hear at the beginning. Then use the words to answer the five riddles.

○ A **blend** is two or three consonants sounded together.

___ apes

___ og

___ ee

___ ain

You can eat us.
We may be green, blue, white, or red.
We grow on vines.
_____
We are _____.

___ uit

I am green.
I am in your yard.
Birds stay in me.
_____
I am a _____.

I am at the store.
I am good to eat.
I help make you big.
_____
I am _____.

I can be small.
You can play with me.
I say, "Choo, choo."
_____
I am a _____.

I can jump and hop.
You find me in a pond.
I eat bugs.
_____
I am a _____.

Directions: Circle the word that names the picture.

grapes

grass

grade

trim

truck

train

trade

trap

tree

drive

drum

drink

from

frost

fruit

train

truck

trick

dress

drapes

drum

gray

grass

grab

Directions: Find the blend in each word, and print its letters on the line.

bring _____

fry _____

trip _____

grade _____

drive _____

brave _____

trick _____

grain _____

bride _____

crumb _____

cross _____

brick _____

trade _____

free _____

price _____

_____

- - - - - - - - - - - - - - - - -

_____
_____

Directions: Print the blend that stands for the sound you hear at the beginning of the name of each picture.

_____ _____ _____
- - - - - - - - - - - - - - -
_____ _____ _____

_____ _____ _____
- - - - - - - - - - - - - - -
_____ _____ _____

Directions: Read the sentences that are started for you. Circle the word that belongs in each sentence, and print it on the line.

_____
- - - - - - - - -

1. Cliff will ride on his red _____ .   slip   sled

- - - - - - - - -

2. Brad broke the blue _____ .   please   plate

- - - - - - - - -

3. Jean gave Glen a _____ .   plum   play

- - - - - - - - -

4. Deb's dog is _____ and white.   block   black

- - - - - - - - -

5. The _____ are in the pots.   plants   play

- - - - - - - - -

6. Dad is _____ to be home.   glide   glad

- - - - - - - - -

7. We can see the _____ on the hill.   flag   flap

Directions: Read each riddle, and print the answer. The pictures will help you.

I tick-tock the time.

Sometimes I chime.

What am I?

_____

_ _ _ _ _ _ _ _ _ _

High up on a pole

I flap and I blow.

What am I?

_____

_ _ _ _ _ _ _ _ _ _

I fly way up high.

Look for me in the sky.

What am I?

_____

_ _ _ _ _ _ _ _ _ _

I grow from a seed.

I am not a weed.

What am I?

_____

_ _ _ _ _ _ _ _ _ _

Directions: Find the word in the list at the right that will complete each sentence. Then print it on the line.

_____
_ _ _ _ _ _ _ _ _ _

1. Mom will use the rake on the _____ . clap

_____
_ _ _ _ _ _ _ _ _ _

2. My boat can _____ on the lake. glass

_____
_ _ _ _ _ _ _ _ _ _

3. Baby likes to _____ her hands. float

_____
_ _ _ _ _ _ _ _ _ _

4. The milk is in the _____ . clock

_____
_ _ _ _ _ _ _ _ _ _

5. Did the cut on his hand _____ ? grass

_____
_ _ _ _ _ _ _ _ _ _

6. A _____ tells us the time. blocks

_____
_ _ _ _ _ _ _ _ _ _

7. Glen made a house with his _____ . bleed

Directions: Say the name of each picture. Print the blend that stands for the sound you hear at the beginning of its name.

Directions: Print the name of each picture on the line.

_____ _____ _____ _____

_____ _____ _____ _____

Directions: Find the word that belongs in each sentence, and print it on the line.

1. Did you see the _____ fly over the pond?

    from   crow   frost

2. The dog is _____ and white.

    blade   bleed   black

3. Brett came home and cut the _____ .

    grass   grab   grape

4. The meat is on the _____ .

    plate   play   plum

5. Fran likes to beat the _____ .

    drum   dress   drink

6. Glen will be _____ to get the prize.

    grade   glad   glass

_____
- -
_____

Directions: Say the name of each picture. Print the blend that stands for the sound you hear at the beginning. The list of blends will help you.

sc	st	sp	sn	squ
scr	str	sl	sm	sw

- - - - - - -
_____

- - - - - - -
_____

- - - - - - -
_____

- - - - - - -
_____

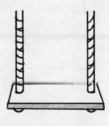

- - - - - - -
_____

- - - - - - -
_____

- - - - - - -
_____

- - - - - - -
_____

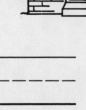

- - - - - - -
_____

- - - - - - -
_____

- - - - - - -
_____

- - - - - - -
_____

LESSON 40: S blends **79**

Directions: Read each sentence that is started for you. Find the word in the list that belongs in the sentence, and print it on the line.

1. Do not _____ the milk.   skate

2. Green means go, and red means _____ .   spill

3. Can you _____ on the ice?   stop

4. Steff saw a _____ near the barn.   skip

5. I can _____ those nice flowers.   smell

6. Greg will dive and _____ in the lake.   swim

7. It is fun to _____ rope.   snake

Directions: Circle the name of each picture.

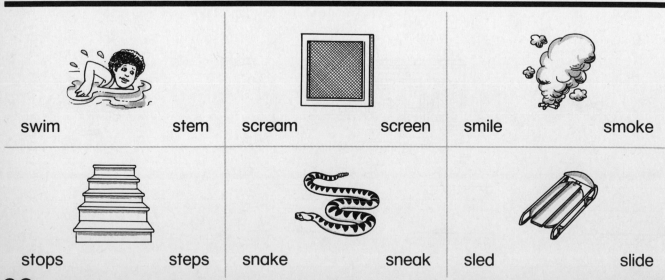

swim	stem	scream	screen	smile	smoke
stops	steps	snake	sneak	sled	slide

80 LESSON 40: S blends

Directions: Read each riddle. Circle the answer, and print it on the line.

All mail needs these. What are they?	We can ride on it. What is it?	We put things in it. What is it?
stamps stumps	string swing	skunk trunk
We can eat it. What is it?	It hides your face. What is it?	We can sleep in it. What is it?
toast list	task mask	tent plant
We put it in a pail. What is it?	Fish swim in it. What is it?	We drink it. What is it?
stand sand	tank wink	silk milk
We have two of these. What are they?	It is a penny. What is it?	It can float. What is it?
bands hands	cent went	raft left

Directions: Say the name of each picture. Print the final blend to complete each word. The first one is done for you.

ring	li____	sku____
de____	sta____	te____
po____	ra____	mi____
ne____	swi____	tru____

Directions: Read each sentence. Change the blend in the word at the right to make a new word that belongs in the sentence. Print the word on the line.

1. Grandma likes to cut the _____ .   glass

2. We must cut the meat on the _____ .   skate

3. Do not play in the _____ .   greet

4. The robins made a nest in the _____ .   free

5. It is fun to _____ rope.   just

6. I will help Fran _____ the steps.   sleep

7. Fred likes to play _____ on us.   sticks

8. I had a _____ of milk for dinner.   brass

9. Steve can _____ his top.   skin

10. Last week I had a funny _____ .   scream

11. The _____ ate all the grain.   grows

12. Jim prints with his _____ hand.   lend

Directions: Circle the blend that will complete the unfinished word in each sentence. Print the blend on the line.

1. We _____ ile when we are happy.   sn   sm   sp

2. Clem _____ oke the glass plate.   sl   sk   br

3. When we a _____ for something we say please.   ft   sk   sp

4. The cat went up the _____ ee.   tr   fr   str

5. Gail likes to _____ im in the lake.   cr   sc   sw

6. Steff sped down the hill on the _____ ed.   sl   squ   pr

Directions: Use the blend at the right to make a word that belongs in each sentence. Print it on the line.

1. The green _____ sat near the pond.   fr

2. We drink _____ from a glass.   lk

3. The class painted the _____ pole.   fl

4. Do not leave your _____ on the steps.   sk

5. My house is on this _____ .   str

6. Scott is tall and _____ .   sl

Directions: Circle each word in which **Y** stands for a sound almost like long **E**.

baby	cry	happy	why
try	lady	candy	tiny
Patty	sandy	shy	puppy
penny	Jimmy	funny	Billy
try	dry	buggy	my
sleepy	sunny	fly	Betty

1. Jane went to get a box of candy.

2. The puppy bumped into the tray.

3. Peggy will play with the baby.

4. Did you see the funny man cry?

5. Tom will get a bunny for his birthday.

6. Betty and Timmy will fry the fish.

7. My little kitty is in its box.

8. Kate lost a penny and a dime.

9. Andy will dry the dishes.

10. Ginny is a happy girl.

Directions: Circle each word in which **Y** stands for a sound almost like long **I**.

try	Teddy	sly	why	funny
bunny	dry	candy	rocky	my
Jenny	windy	by	sky	sunny
fry	fly	happy	Sally	cry
needy	lucky	shy	puppy	Billy

1. Did you see the sly fox?

2. I will try to win the prize.

3. Why did the bunny run?

4. Betty helps Tommy dry the dishes.

5. Vicky will fry eggs for lunch.

6. The puppy will try to run.

7. Gene is shy in school.

8. Have you seen my little red top?

9. See the plane fly in the sky.

10. I set the shell by the box.

_____

- - - - - - - - - - - - - - - -

_____

Directions: Find a **Y** word at the bottom of the page that belongs in each sentence. Print it on the line.

1. _____ are you crying?

2. The name of the boy is _____ .

3. Tony's _____ dug a hole.

4. Molly will _____ to win.

5. The dog did a _____ trick.

6. We will be _____ inside the tent.

Directions: Read the word in each baseball. If the **Y** stands for a long **I** sound, color the ball yellow. If it stands for a long **E** sound, color it orange.

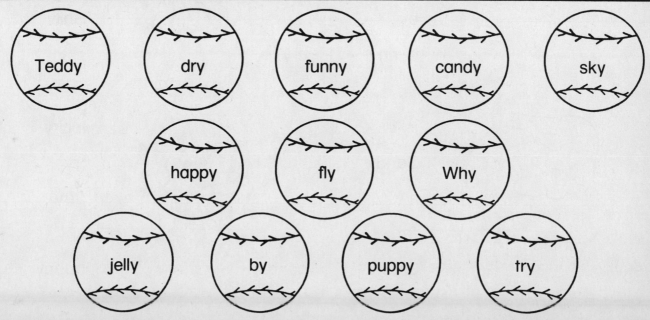

Teddy   dry   funny   candy   sky

happy   fly   Why

jelly   by   puppy   try

Directions: Look at the picture in each box. Say its name. Read the words in the list. Circle each word that has the same sound of **Y** as the name of the picture.

bunny	baby my fly fifty funny
pony	sky sunny fairy cry Bobby
fly	dolly try sly kitty dry
puppy	lady penny shy fry happy
lily	why silly baby by bunny
cry	my sixty fly Sally sky
sky	jelly Sandy my fry cry
candy	lucky try fifty sky puppy

_____

- -

Directions: Circle the word that completes each sentence.

1.	Vic and Joe like to eat	cheese.	sheets.	chase.
2.	We played in the sand at the	bunch.	bench.	beach.
3.	We will paint the house	wheeze.	whine.	white.
4.	Did you brush your	then?	teeth?	there?
5.	We went to the pet	shop.	shone.	thin.
6.	In my lunch I have a big	cheek.	with.	peach.
7.	I help wash the	dash.	splashes.	dishes.
8.	Ruth fell when the bike lost a	whale.	wheel.	shell.
9.	Josh ran up the	path.	with.	this.
10.	It is nice to sit in the	fresh.	shut.	shade.

Directions: Find three words from the top of the page that begin with **ch**, **wh**, **th**, and **sh.** Print them on the lines beside the correct consonant digraph.

ch

th

wh

sh

Directions: Circle the word that will complete each sentence.

1. I hope the sun will (shine, chin).

2. (Where, This) did you go?

3. Mother wants us to (thing, think).

4. I (chose, chair) the big prize.

5. (This, When) is my best work.

6. Please get (that, what) glass.

7. (What, That) time is it?

8. (They, The) are here.

9. We will go (when, then) the bell rings.

10. Did you have (church, chicken) for dinner?

11. Have you had a ride on a (chip, ship)?

12. Do not drop that (dish, wish).

13. Sally likes to play with the (blocks, docks).

14. Will you (dish, brush) my suit?

15. Bill did not (catch, pinch) the ball.

16. We went to the (shop, chop).

_____

===

Directions: If the consonant digraph is at the beginning of a word, print the word in the first column. If it is in the middle, print the word in the second. If it is at the end, print the word in the third column.

===

cheer	quack	reach	stuck	riches	when	shine
brushing	kicking	peach	dishes	thank	wishing	teaching
fish	bench	why	chin	clothing	shell	bath

BEGINNING	MIDDLE	END

Directions: Say the name of each picture. Circle the letters that stand for the consonant digraph you hear.

Picture	Choices	Picture	Choices	Picture	Choices
(shoe)	th sh ck ch wh	(thimble)	th sh ck ch wh	(wheat)	th sh ck ch wh
(truck)	th sh ck ch wh	(whale)	th sh ck ch wh	(thumb)	th sh ck ch wh
(shell)	th sh ck ch wh	(duck)	th sh ck ch wh	(chair)	th sh ck ch wh
(chain)	th sh ck ch wh	13	th sh ck ch wh	(clock)	th sh ck ch wh

_____

- -

_____

Directions: Read the sentences. Then print the number of the sentence that tells about the picture in the circle below it.

1. John has a knot in the rope.
2. I know what is in the box.
3. Joan can twist the knob.

○   ○

1. Tad needs a patch.
2. Mom cut it with a knife.
3. Thad will knock down the pile.

○   ○

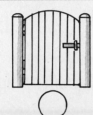

1. Cal has a knapsack.
2. Joe knocks on the gate.
3. Grandma likes to knit.

○   ○

Directions: Find the word in the list that answers each riddle. Print it on the line.

knife	knot	know	knit	knob	knee

1. Something that can cut.

_____

2. Something Grandma did with the yarn.

_____

3. Something you can bend.

_____

4. Something you can tie.

_____

Directions: Circle the word that completes each sentence, and print it on the line.

1. Nan will tie the rope in a _____.   knit   knot

2. Put the _____ next to the plate.   knife   knit

3. Grandma can _____ hats for us.   knit   knew

4. The door has a shiny brass _____.   knob   knit

5. Jack cut it with his _____.   knit   knife

6. Bob may fall and skin his _____.   knee   knob

7. Do you _____ Russ?   know   knit

8. Can you _____ on one knee?   kneel   knew

Directions: Think of a word beginning with **kn** that rhymes with the given word. Print it on the line.

snow	sit	feel
_____	_____	_____
block	wife	blew
_____	_____	_____
cob	see	hot
_____	_____	_____

Directions: Find the name of each picture in the list of words. Print the name on the line below the picture.

apple	eagle	needle	people
candle	buckle	handle	thimble
steeple	bottle	table	bubbles

Directions: Find the word that completes each sentence, and print it on the line.

1. The _____ is boiling on the stove.

pickle

2. Vicky got the pretty _____ at the beach.

saddle

3. The _____ of the pan is made of wood.

kettle

4. Jack tried to jump over the _____ but fell in.

puddle

5. I put a _____ in my lunchbox.

pebble

6. Kathy put the _____ on the pony.

handle

1. Linda likes to _____ the baby.

candles

2. Please try not to _____ in your seat.

rattle

3. I lit the _____ on the cake.

ripples

4. The _____ is up in the sky.

wiggle

5. The baby likes to play with the _____ .

tickle

6. The rock made _____ in the pond.

eagle

Directions: Find the word that completes each sentence, and print it on the line.

wrap

wren

write

1. Ed and Dan will _____ the big gift.

    wrench

2. The bus went the _____ way.

    wrote

3. Who _____ that letter to you?

    wren

4. Two new trucks had a _____ .

    wreck

5. The _____ sat on the eggs in the nest.

    wrong

6. When Jean fell she broke her _____ .

    wrap

7. Sue will _____ to Jenny.

    write

8. Mom used a _____ to fix the pipe.

    wriggle

9. The pup can _____ under the fence.

    wrist

Directions: Find the answer to each riddle in the list of words at the top. Print the answer next to the correct numeral at the bottom.

wren   wrecker   wrinkle   wrist

wrench   wreath   writer   typewriter

1. I am round and green.
   You can hang me up.
   What am I?

2. I can fly.
   I like to sing.
   What is my name?

3. I am next to a hand.
   I can twist and bend.
   What am I called?

4. I am a big truck.
   I tow things away.
   What am I called?

5. I mess up your clothes.
   You can iron me away.
   What am I?

6. I am a useful tool.
   I can fix things.
   What is my name?

7. I can print.
   People strike my keys.
   What is my name?

8. I am one who writes.
   I can make up tall tales.
   What am I called?

1. _____

2. _____

3. _____

4. _____

5. _____

6. _____

7. _____

8. _____

 LESSON 49: Consonant digraph WR

Directions: Find the word that completes each sentence, and print it on the line.

knows	knock	knitted	doorknob
wrapped	wrong	knot	wring
wrist	written		

1. We had to _____ out the wet suits.

2. Cathy _____ some red-and-white socks.

3. Brad _____ the gift with blue ribbon.

4. Mandy _____ how to add and subtract.

5. Did you _____ at the front door?

6. The note is neatly _____ .

7. The _____ is made of brass.

8. It is _____ to tell a lie.

9. A _____ is in the string.

10. Rick fell and sprained his _____ .

Directions: Say the name of each picture. Listen for the consonant digraphs. Do you hear them at the beginning, middle, or end? Print the digraphs in the correct blocks.

LESSON 50: Reviewing consonant digraphs SH; TH; WH; CH; CK; KN; WR

Directions: Read each riddle. Find the answer in the list at the right, and print the numeral of the answer on the line.

It is something we can eat. _____   1.   sheet

It is on your bed. _____   2.   brush

You can sit on it. _____   3.   whale

It is something we can use to clean. _____   4.   chair

It lives in the sea. _____   5.   peach

It is wrong to do this. _____   1.   teeth

A bike runs on them. _____   2.   rattle

A king sits on this. _____   3.   wheels

We must brush them each day. _____   4.   cheat

A baby likes to play with it. _____   5.   throne

You may see these on the beach. _____   1.   wheat

We can make rolls from this. _____   2.   peaches

They are red and yellow and grow on trees. _____   3.   shells

Smoke goes up this. _____   4.   clock

It tells time. _____   5.   chimney

Directions: Say the name of each picture. Print the missing letters to complete the word.

eese

ell

app

ock

ite

tru

ink

cand

eel

bott

ain

di es

Directions: Read each sentence. Find a word in the column at the right that will complete the sentence, and print it on the line.

barn

star

car

1. We went for a ride in Mom's _____ .   park

2. The children played in the _____ .   far

3. Is the store _____ away from here?   farm

4. We went to see Grandpa on the _____ .   car

5. The jam is in the _____ .   yard

6. I saw a shiny _____ in the sky.   yarn

7. Did you hear the dog _____ ?   jar

8. The kitten played with the _____ .   harm

9. We like to play in the back _____ .   star

10. The big dog will not _____ you.   bark

Directions: Read the word following each sentence. Change the last letter to make a new word that will finish the sentence, and print it on the line.

1. Fran will mail Dan a _____ .   cart

2. Do not try to read in the _____ .   dart

3. Can you see the _____ in the sky?   start

4. We made funny cards in _____ class.   arm

5. See the goats and pigs in the _____ at the farm.   bark

6. Kate and Bart went to play in the _____ .   part

7. To begin means to _____ .   stars

8. Barb made a scarf with the red _____ .   yard

9. The old car is _____ to start.   harm

Directions: Print two rhyming words under each of the given words.

mark	start	hard
_____	_____	_____
_____	_____	_____

Directions: Answer each riddle by thinking of a word that rhymes with the word following the riddle. Print the word on the line.

Mark and Lori like to play word games. Do you think words are fun?

1. Something to eat.   horn   _____

2. Something on an ox.   born   _____

3. Something we eat with.   cork   _____

4. Something that brings rain.   form   _____

5. Something we play with our pals.   port   _____

6. Some place to shop.   more   _____

7. Something on a rose.   born   _____

8. Something beside the sea.   tore   _____

9. Something in a bottle.   pork   _____

Directions: Circle the name of the picture.

 jab
jar
jay

 yard
yarn
yell

 barn
bark
book

 home
horse
horn

 fifty
forty
fairy

 torch
arch
scorch

 car
card
cost

 come
corn
cart

 store
stand
star

 home
horse
horn

 arm
are
am

 fort
farm
fork

106 LESSON 53: Reviewing AR and OR

Directions: Circle each word with the same sound as the name of the picture.

bird 	turkey	fern
ir	**ur**	**er**
first	curb	batter
fork	purse	letter
skirt	card	hammer
shirt	church	park
girl	fur	clerk

Directions: Find the name of each picture in the words above. Print the names on the lines.

Directions: Circle the name of each picture. Then color the box with the same vowel with **r** as the name.

bird	first	tar
barn	batter	turkey
burn	farm	third

er	or	ir	ir	er	ar	ur	ar	or

hammer	shirt	goat
farmer	skirt	garden
summer	scarf	girl

ir	or	er	ar	ir	ur	ir	or	ur

Directions: Choose the word that completes each sentence and print it on the line.

1. The big white rabbit has white _____ .

far
fur
fist

2. We can hear the birds _____ .

church
cheat
chirp

3. Becky looked for her _____ .

purse
purple
park

4. Peter sent me a _____ for my birthday.

curl
cord
card

5. Wash your hands to kill the _____ .

gets
germs
greens

Directions: In each word find the vowel followed by **r**. Print the two letters next to the word. Then print the numeral of the picture that has the same two letters in its name.

1. car   2. horn   3. bird   4. hammer   5. church

part	_____ _____		storm	_____ _____
verse	_____ _____		her	_____ _____
turn	_____ _____		chirp	_____ _____
perch	_____ _____		burn	_____ _____
pork	_____ _____		park	_____ _____
first	_____ _____		horse	_____ _____
party	_____ _____		fur	_____ _____
third	_____ _____		skirt	_____ _____
bark	_____ _____		curb	_____ _____
fern	_____ _____		short	_____ _____

Directions: Circle the letters to finish the word in each sentence. Print the letters on the line.

1. The black horse is in the b _____ n.   ar   or   ur

2. My cat has gray f _____ .   or   ur   ar

3. Peggy sits in the f _____ st seat.   or   ir   ar

4. The c _____ k is in the jug.   ar   er   or

5. Kurt swept the d _____ t away.   ir   or   ar

6. The cl _____ k gave me back a dime.   ar   er   or

7. Karl will be the next batt _____ .   er   ir   or

8. Lorna h _____ t her knee on the swing.   ar   er   ur

Directions: Use the words in the list to answer the riddles.

bark	car	dark	clerk	corn
skirt	park	fur	purse	born

It is part of a dress.	You like to eat it.	Dogs do this.
_____	_____	_____
A rabbit has it.	A person can drive it.	We play games in it.
_____	_____	_____

Directions: Say the name of each picture. Circle the vowel followed by **r** that you hear in the name.

ar	or	ar
or	ir	er
ur	ar	or

er	ar	or
or	er	ar
ar	or	ir

ar	or	er
or	ur	or
ir	ar	ar

ur	ar	ir
or	er	or
ar	or	ar

Directions: Read the sentences and do what they tell you to do. Then draw a line under each word that has the letters **ar, or, ir, er,** or **ur.**

1. Do you see the skirt? Circle the skirt. Color the skirt red.

2. See the letter. Color it green. Make a black dot near it.

3. Can you see the fern? Color it green. Draw a line under it.

4. Look at the girl. Color her hair red. Color her scarf blue.

5. See the barn. Make a little black **X** under it. Color the barn red.

6. Do you see the corn? Color the corn yellow. Draw a box around the corn.

7. See the star. Color it blue. Make two red dots near the star.

8. Look at the turkey. Make a blue **X** under it. Color it red and purple.

_____

Directions: Print the word that means the same as the two words given.

she will   **she'll**

The short way to write **she will** is **she'll**.

_____

you'll   they'll   she'll   we'll   I'll   he'll

I will   _____   he will   _____

we will   _____   they will   _____

she will   _____   you will   _____

Directions: Print the short form of the two underlined words in each sentence.

1.   I will go to the store with you.   _____

2.   He will mail the letters.   _____

3.   We will play games with Tom.   _____

4.   They will plant the tree.   _____

5.   You will have a surprise this week.   _____

6.   She will win the prize.   _____

Directions: Print the word that means the same as the two words given.

can not   **can't**

The short way to write **can not** is **can't**.

| can't | couldn't | weren't | don't |
| didn't | aren't | isn't | won't |

are not _____   do not _____

did not _____   will not _____

were not _____   is not _____

could not _____   can not _____

Directions: Print the two words that mean the same as the underlined word.

1. Jane <u>isn't</u> going with you.   _____

2. We <u>haven't</u> a big box.   _____

3. Tim <u>didn't</u> clean the yard.   _____

4. Kathy <u>doesn't</u> need her coat.   _____

5. Andy <u>won't</u> like the show.   _____

6. <u>Aren't</u> you in third grade?   _____

LESSON 57: Contractions with not

Directions: Read each sentence. Circle the two words that can be made into one of the contractions at the top of the page. Print the contraction on the line.

he is = he's   That is = That's

she is = she's   it is = it's

It is Danny's birthday.

What a surprise he is going to get!

Blanch has a gift, but she is hiding it.

Norm knows what the gift is, but he is not telling.

What do you think it is going to be?

Look at the picture at the top.
That is what Danny wants the most.

Directions: Read each sentence. Print the contraction that has the same meaning as the underlined words. The words on the circus tent will help you.

You have = You've   I have = I've

We have = We've   They have = They've

I have made you smile.

_____

_ _ _ _ _ _ _ _ _ _ _ _ _

_____ made you smile.

We have shown you tricks.

_____

_ _ _ _ _ _ _ _ _ _ _ _ _

_____ shown you tricks.

They have tossed a ball with their noses.

_____

_ _ _ _ _ _ _ _ _ _ _ _ _

_____ tossed a ball with their noses.

You have had a good time.

_____

_ _ _ _ _ _ _ _ _ _ _ _ _

_____ had a good time.

Directions: Print the two words that mean the same as the underlined word in the sentence.

1. <u>We're</u> going to pick some berries. _____

2. <u>Let's</u> go on the bus. _____

3. <u>I'm</u> going to take a basket. _____

4. "<u>They're</u> baked," Tom cried. _____

5. <u>We'll</u> go to the picnic today. _____

6. <u>You're</u> the one she asked for. _____

Directions: Print the contraction that means the same as the two given words.

you are _____   she is _____

I am _____   it is _____

let us _____   they are _____

we are _____   we will _____

he is _____   they will _____

Directions: Print the number of each contraction next to the words that have the same meaning. The first one is done for you.

1.	we're	____	I am	9.	don't	____	is not
2.	you'll	_1_	we are	10.	she's	____	you are
3.	it's	____	will not	11.	you're	____	I will
4.	can't	____	he is	12.	isn't	____	we will
5.	I'm	____	you will	13.	she'll	____	do not
6.	he's	____	let us	14.	we'll	____	I have
7.	won't	____	can not	15.	I'll	____	she will
8.	let's	____	it is	16.	I've	____	she is

Directions: Circle the word that will complete each sentence. Print it on the line.

1. Why _____ you skate with Carla and me?

isn't
don't
you're

2. Pam said, " _____ go to the park."

Let's
I'm
It's

3. I think _____ going to be late.

won't
we've
we're

4. _____ help you make the puppet.

I'm
I'll
I've

5. _____ won the baseball game!

Can't
You're
We've

118   LESSON 59: Contractions

Directions: Print the two words that mean the same as the contraction.

I've _____   didn't _____

he'll _____   you've _____

they're _____   let's _____

isn't _____   won't _____

hasn't _____   I'll _____

Directions: Print the shortened form of the underlined words in each sentence on the line.

_____

1. <u>He will</u> read a story to the class.

_____

2. <u>Let us</u> start the baseball game.

_____

3. <u>You are</u> a good reader, Jess.

_____

4. Jane <u>has not</u> missed a day of school.

_____

5. <u>He is</u> feeling well today.

_____

6. <u>I will</u> help if you let me.

Directions: Print the contraction that means the same as the two words you see.

I have _____   can not _____

do not _____   could not _____

let us _____   there is _____

did not _____   you have _____

Directions: Circle the correct word for each sentence. Print it on the line.

1. _____ a surprise for Lee.   Didn't   It's

2. _____ my new bike.   That's   Isn't

3. Beth _____ be here today.   won't   you're

4. Chuck _____ need my help.   aren't   doesn't

5. Gus _____ going to play with us.   isn't   don't

6. _____ have to hurry home for lunch.   They're   You'll

7. _____ going to the park to play.   We're   Don't

8. Jenny _____ come to the party.   you're   couldn't

Directions: Choose the correct word, and print it on the line. Color one or two pictures in each box according to your answer.

○ If a word ends in **x, z, ss, sh,** or **ch,** usually add **es** to make it mean more than one.

1. Rick broke two of Mom's yellow

   dish   dishes

   _____ .

2. We have candy in two

   box   boxes

   _____ .

3. Jack's mother gave him a

   cap   caps

   _____ .

4. Look at those shiny

   star   stars

   _____ !

5. "Peep, peep," said the two

   chick   chicks

   _____ .

6. We like to eat fresh

   peach   peaches

   _____ .

7. Sue will use a hair

   brush   brushes

   _____ .

8. Just look at those

   dog   dogs

   _____ .

9. The box was used for

   mitten   mittens

   _____ .

10. At the zoo we saw some

    seal   seals

    _____ .

Directions: Read each shopping list. Finish each word by adding the ending **s** or **es**. Print it on the line.

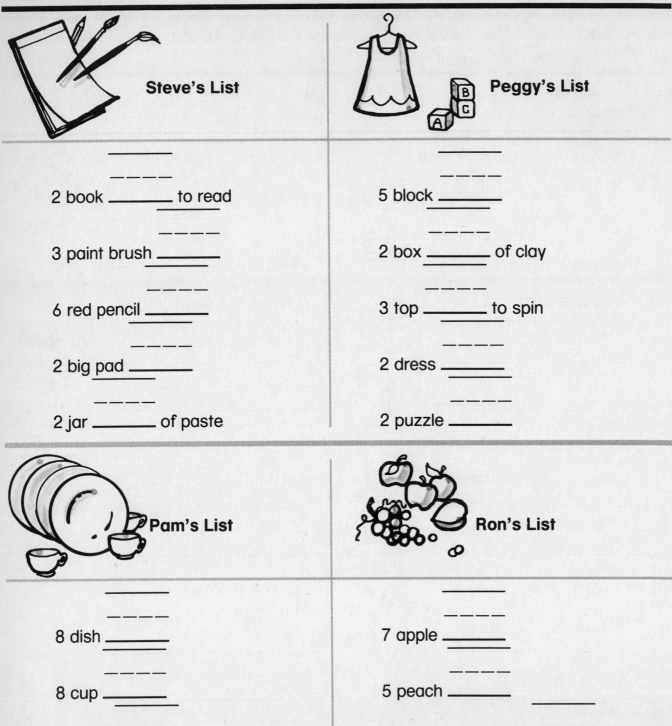

Steve's List

2 book _____ to read

3 paint brush _____

6 red pencil _____

2 big pad _____

2 jar _____ of paste

Peggy's List

5 block _____

2 box _____ of clay

3 top _____ to spin

2 dress _____

2 puzzle _____

Pam's List

8 dish _____

8 cup _____

4 glass _____

2 salad bowl _____

2 patch _____ for jeans

Ron's List

7 apple _____

5 peach _____

4 cheese sandwich _____

2 car wax _____

2 bunch _____ of grapes

_____

Directions: Add the ending **ing** to each base word. Print the new word.

sleep _____   jump _____

brush _____   play _____

help _____   start _____

hunt _____   fish _____

work _____   turn _____

Directions: Complete each sentence by adding the ending **ing** to the word following the sentence. Print the new word on the line.

1. The children are _____ for the bus.   wait

2. Dora and Mark are _____ rope.   jump

3. She is _____ at the blue coat.   look

4. Mother is _____ Jane's hair.   brush

5. Bart is _____ to help us.   stay

6. Terry is _____ the kitten.   keep

LESSON 62: Inflectional ending -ING   **123**

Directions: Add the ending **ed** to each base word. Print the new word on the line.

rain _____   pack _____   help _____

_ _ _ _ _ _ _ _ _ _ _ _ _   _ _ _ _ _ _ _ _ _ _ _ _ _   _ _ _ _ _ _ _ _ _ _ _ _ _

leap _____   wish _____   ask _____

_ _ _ _ _ _ _ _ _ _ _ _ _   _ _ _ _ _ _ _ _ _ _ _ _ _   _ _ _ _ _ _ _ _ _ _ _ _ _

Directions: Choose a word from the first exercise to complete each sentence. Print it on the line.

_ _ _ _ _ _ _ _ _ _ _ _ _

1. The frog _____ over a rock in the garden.

_ _ _ _ _ _ _ _ _ _ _ _ _

2. Chuck _____ fix the desk.

_ _ _ _ _ _ _ _ _ _ _ _ _

3. I _____ my bag for the trip.

_ _ _ _ _ _ _ _ _ _ _ _ _

4. Patsy _____ for a big red dog.

_ _ _ _ _ _ _ _ _ _ _ _ _

5. It _____ on the first day.

_ _ _ _ _ _ _ _ _ _ _ _ _

6. Jane _____ the rain would stop.

Directions: Print the base word on the line.

locked _____   marched _____   dreamed _____

_ _ _ _ _ _ _ _ _ _ _ _ _   _ _ _ _ _ _ _ _ _ _ _ _ _   _ _ _ _ _ _ _ _ _ _ _ _ _

played _____   cleaned _____   passed _____

_ _ _ _ _ _ _ _ _ _ _ _ _   _ _ _ _ _ _ _ _ _ _ _ _ _   _ _ _ _ _ _ _ _ _ _ _ _ _

_____

- -

_____

Directions: Add either **es** or **ed** to the base word to complete each unfinished word.

_____
- - - - - - - - -
1. Jean brush _____ her hair until it shines.

_____
- - - - - - - - -
2. When Carlos miss _____ the bus, he walks.

_____
- - - - - - - - -
3. The dog bark _____ when the car came near.

_____
- - - - - - - - -
4. Randy cheer _____ until his throat was sore.

_____
- - - - - - - - -
5. The girls play _____ ball in the school yard.

_____
- - - - - - - - -
6. See the bee as it buzz _____ near the bushes.

_____
- - - - - - - - -
7. Art pass _____ Jack and won the race.

Directions: Add **s** or **es** to each base word, and print it on the line.

see	beach	fish	branch	mail	line

_____   _____
- - - - - - - - -   - - - - - - - - -
_____   _____
- - - - - - - - -   - - - - - - - - -
_____   _____

Directions: Circle the word that belongs in each sentence. Print it on the line.

1. Fred _____ the chickens.

   feed
   feeding
   feeds

2. Day after day that truck _____ his house.

   passes
   passing
   pass

3. A big boat is _____ on the lake.

   floating
   floats
   floated

4. Mr. Gray went _____ after dinner.

   walked
   walking
   walk

5. Sally _____ a puppy to care for.

   wants
   want
   wanting

6. He _____ faster than Billy and Dan.

   work
   working
   worked

7. Peggy is _____ Sue with her reading.

   helped
   helps
   helping

8. The horse likes _____ fences.

   jump
   jumps
   jumping

9. Mother _____ for her blue pen.

   look
   looking
   looked

10. Arthur went _____ with his father.

    fished
    fish
    fishing

LESSON 63: Reviewing endings -S; -ES; -ED; -ING

_____

- -

_____

Directions: Add the ending **ing** to the base word following each sentence. Then print the word on the line to complete the sentence.

○ When a short-vowel word ends in a single consonant, usually double the consonant before adding **ing.**

1. The girls were _____ to the park. run

2. Here comes a rabbit _____ in the grass. hop

3. Grace is _____ her pet rabbit. feed

4. She likes to go _____ in the lake. swim

5. Bert is _____ hot dogs for the party. roast

6. Mary's dog is _____ for a treat. beg

7. The boys are _____ near the lake. jog

8. See the pony _____ down the road. trot

9. Carl likes to go _____ with Father. camp

10. Ted is _____ for a gift. shop

11. The team with red caps is _____ . win

Directions: Add the ending **ed** to the word following each sentence. Print it on the line.

○ When a short-vowel word ends in a single consonant, usually double the consonant before adding **ed.**

1. Glenn _____ the ball.   drop

2. Joan _____ to the little girl.   nod

3. Lori _____ her mother for a bike.   beg

4. The big black dog _____ his tail.   wag

5. Sue _____ up her little brother.   pick

6. Jane _____ her hand into the pail.   dip

7. When the bell rang, we _____ printing.   stop

8. The dog _____ up on the seat.   jump

9. We _____ the car with a clean rag.   scrub

Directions: Add the endings **ed** and **ing** to each word.

wag	clean	hop
_____	_____	_____
_____	_____	_____
_____	_____	_____

_____

_ _ _ _ _ _ _ _ _ _ _ _ _ _ _ _ _ _

_____

Directions: Add the ending **ing** or **ed** to each word. Print the new words on the lines.

Don't Forget—If a word ends with a silent **e**, drop the **e** before adding **ing** or **ed**.

ing

ed

hope		close	
get		joke	
eat		bake	
drive		smile	
save		help	
camp		skate	
sit		trim	
bat		rub	
hike		pass	

Directions: Add the ending **ing** to each base word.

Add ing.

ride	_____	fry	_____
rub	_____	hide	_____
frame	_____	dig	_____
take	_____	jump	_____
poke	_____	whip	_____
pack	_____	quit	_____

Directions: Add the ending **ed** to each base word.

Add ed.

pin	_____	rock	_____
chase	_____	hop	_____
march	_____	bake	_____
wish	_____	drop	_____
tap	_____	quack	_____
hope	_____	like	_____

_____
_ _
_____

Directions: Add the ending at the top of the column to each word below it.

ing	ed	s or es
wave	skip	peach
_____	_____	_____
drop	like	cross
_____	_____	_____
smile	press	tree
_____	_____	_____

Directions: Complete each sentence by adding the correct ending to the base word. Print the new word on the line.

1. My _____ is much better this year.   read

2. Father said that I may go _____ .   swim

3. The old horse _____ home.   trot

4. We are _____ a birthday cake.   bake

5. Mr. Gray _____ five boxes of stamps.   save

6. Sally is _____ the big bus.   drive

7. Mom is _____ me to fish.   teach

Directions: Add the correct endings to the words in the list, and use them to complete the sentences.

skate   cut   cook

share   ask   spell

1. Mary Ann _____ the words for me.

2. Last night Jack _____ for a story.

3. I see children _____ on the ice.

4. Joan is _____ roses for Grandmother.

5. Each day Fred _____ his lunch with Bert.

6. Mom and Dad are _____ dinner for us.

Directions: Draw a box around each base word.

dressed	buzzes	jumped	plays	puffed
brushing	crying	loading	boxes	dishes
cleaned	parking	wished	stayed	swimming
snapping	planned	cooking	drives	drops

_____

_ _ _ _ _ _ _ _ _ _ _ _ _ _ _ _ _ _ _

Directions: Add the ending **ful** to each base word. Then use the new words to complete the sentences below.

hopeful
The ending is **ful.**
The base word is **hope.**

care	help	play
_____	_____	_____
pain	rest	thank
_____	_____	_____

1. Jack was _____ for his gifts.

2. Be _____ when you cross the street.

3. Jean had a _____ nap.

4. The _____ puppy begged for food.

5. The bad tooth was _____ .

6. Sam likes to be _____ at work.

Directions: Draw a box around each base word.

painful	hopeful	restful	grateful
thankful	cheerful	playful	careful

Directions: Add **less** or **ness** to the words at the top of the page. Then use the new words in the sentences below.

Add **less**.		Add **ness**.
sleep		thick
care		neat
harm		sick
fear		sad

1. "He will not bite you," said Liz. "Spot is _____."

2. Ray was _____ and lost his books.

3. _____ kept Ted out of school for three weeks.

4. The _____ of his coat kept him from getting hurt.

5. The _____ baby did not take her nap.

6. Miss King gave Pat a good grade in _____.

7. The lion is brave and _____.

8. Her face was full of _____.

_____

_ _ _ _ _ _ _ _ _ _ _ _ _ _ _ _ _ _ _ _

Directions: Add the ending **ly** to each base word.

quickly
The ending is **ly.**
The base word is **quick.**

glad _____   swift _____

soft _____   brave _____

neat _____   cruel _____

bad _____   slow _____

Directions: Circle each **ly** ending in the sentences. Then print the base words on the lines.

1. The children worked quickly.

2. The fireman acted bravely.

3. Mary was playing the music softly.

4. The king spoke wisely.

5. Jan and Dean have a lovely home.

6. The umpire ruled fairly.

Directions: In each box, match the base word in the first column with the new word in the second column. Print the correct numeral on the line. The first one is done for you.

_2_ quick	1. slowly		____ glad	1. softly
____ sweet	2. quickly		____ soft	2. nearly
____ slow	3. sweetly		____ near	3. lovely
____ loud	4. loudly		____ love	4. gladly

____ use	1. playful		____ help	1. armful
____ play	2. handful		____ hope	2. cupful
____ cheer	3. useful		____ arm	3. helpful
____ hand	4. cheerful		____ cup	4. hopeful

____ home	1. cheerless		____ care	1. fearless
____ use	2. homeless		____ sleeve	2. jobless
____ wire	3. useless		____ fear	3. careless
____ cheer	4. wireless		____ job	4. sleeveless

____ like	1. sweetness		____ good	1. softness
____ sad	2. sickness		____ dark	2. nearness
____ sweet	3. likeness		____ near	3. darkness
____ sick	4. sadness		____ soft	4. goodness

_____

- - - - - - - - - - - - - - - -

Directions: Add the ending from the list at the right that will complete the unfinished word in each sentence.

ly	**ful**
less	**ness**

1. Jane is a very friend _____ girl.

2. It is care _____ to leave things on the steps.

3. Our kitten is very play _____ .

4. Our car stopped when we were near _____ home.

5. Sing and play your sad _____ away.

6. We like pals who are cheer _____ .

Directions: Read the words in the list. Print the correct word below each definition.

| homeless | safely | playful | harmful |
| sickness | sadly | neatness | helpful |

with no home

_____

full of play

_____

with harm

_____

being of help

_____

with sadness

_____

in a safe way

_____

being sick

_____

being neat

_____

Directions: Add the ending to each base word. Print the new word on the line.

ly

soft _____

glad _____

ful

help _____

cheer _____

less

home _____

pain _____

ness

sad _____

sick _____

Directions: Add the correct ending to each base word to complete the sentence.

1. Spot is a very _____ puppy.   play

2. The clean dishes are _____ .   spot

3. Mark will _____ help you.   glad

4. We were in _____ after the storm.   dark

5. Drink this _____ of milk.   glass

6. Ted mixed the cake batter with a _____ mixer.   cord

7. The box was _____ full.   near

_____

- -

═══════════════════════

Directions: Add the endings **er** and **est** to each word. Print the new words on the lines.

	er	**est**
near		
long		
fast		
dark		
clean		
thick		
deep		
soft		
red		

Directions: Draw a picture to show the meaning of each word.

long   longer   longest

Directions: Complete each sentence by adding **er** or **est** to the base word. Use **er** to tell about two things. Use **est** to tell about more than two things.

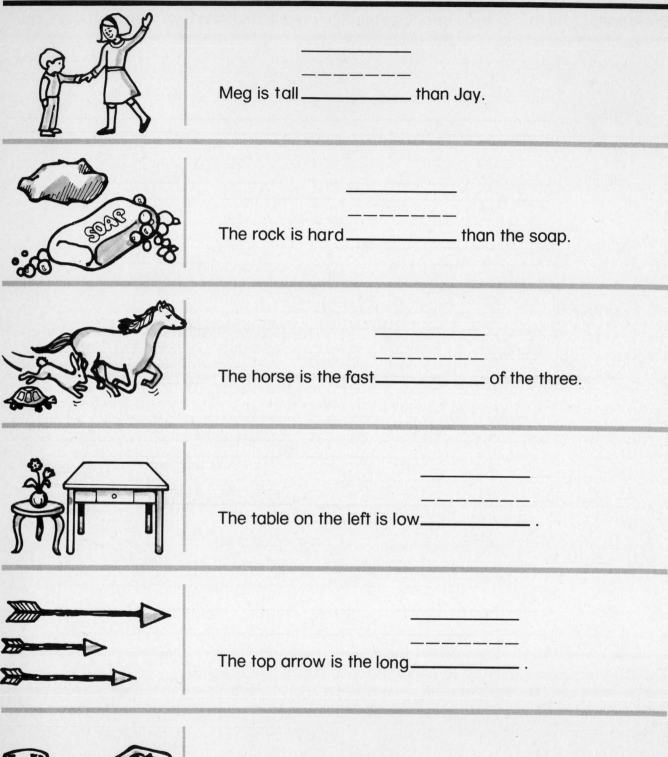

Meg is tall _____ than Jay.

The rock is hard _____ than the soap.

The horse is the fast _____ of the three.

The table on the left is low _____ .

The top arrow is the long _____ .

Ice is cold _____ than water.

_____

- -

_____

Directions: Add the endings **er** and **est** to the words in the list. Print the new words on the lines.

○ When a word ends in **y** after a consonant, change the **y** to **i** before adding the ending **er** or **est**.

er	est
silly	
happy	
lazy	
fluffy	

Directions: Complete each sentence by adding **er** or **est** to the base word at the right.

1. That is the _____ dog I have ever seen.   funny

2. The blue dress is _____ than the red one.   pretty

3. Mark tried to tell the _____ story.   silly

4. We must wait for a _____ day to sail.   windy

5. This road is _____ than the one we were on.   bumpy

6. Sally was the _____ one at the big fair.   lucky

Directions: Circle the name of each picture.

○ When a word ends in **y** after a consonant, change the **y** to **i** before adding the ending **es.**

daisy   daisies | cherry   cherries | lily   lilies

Directions: Read each sentence. Use the rule to print the word that will correctly complete the sentence.

1. Joe liked the five little circus _____ .   pony

2. Miss Day asked us to make two _____ .   copy

3. There were three _____ under the bush.   bunny

4. We picked a bunch of _____ .   daisy

5. We liked the two black _____ best.   puppy

6. Dad told us two funny _____ .   story

7. The lady gave Jay ten _____ .   penny

8. Carla went to two _____ on Friday.   party

9. Andy picked _____ in the country.   lily

10. The _____ look like twins.   baby

LESSON 71: Suffix -ES: Words ending in Y

Directions: Change the words to mean more than one.

lady _____

city _____

pony _____

jelly _____

dress _____

box _____

bunny _____

lily _____

candy _____

Directions: Circle the word that belongs in each sentence. Print it on the line.

_____

1. Mary went to two birthday (party - parties).

_____

2. We like to hear Vic read a (story - stories).

_____

3. Nan has fifty (penny - pennies) in the bank.

_____

4. There are pretty (lily - lilies) in the vase.

_____

5. Joe likes to make (cherry - cherries) pie.

Directions: Print the name of each picture.

_____   _____   _____

Directions: Read each sentence. Add the ending **es** to the word at the right to correctly complete the sentence.

1. We will read five new _____ .   story

2. Susan picked some ripe _____ .   cherry

3. Chuck went to three _____ .   party

4. Cindy planted six pots of _____ .   lily

5. The boy spent his ten _____ .   penny

6. Can you name some big _____ ?   city

7. It is fun to pick _____ .   berry

8. Three _____ live on this farm.   family

9. Please, may I see the six _____ ?   puppy

10. Five _____ trotted up the road.   pony

11. Nancy helped the mother with her twin _____ .   baby

12. Gary has three fuzzy little _____ .   bunny

13. We gave the _____ to our friend.   daisy

Directions: Say the name of each picture. Find the word in the list that names it. Print the word on the line.

sail	pay	train	rain
pail	mail	hay	tray
spray	jay	chain	nail

Directions: Read each sentence. Find the word in the list that each sentence tells about. Print it on the line.

○ If a one-part word or syllable has two vowels, the first vowel is usually long and the second one is silent.

chain	stain	mailbox	hay
pail	rain	hair	paint
chair	train	gray	sail

1. I ride on railroad tracks. _____

2. You drop letters in me. _____

3. I am a blend of black and white. _____

4. If I start, you put on a raincoat. _____

5. You can sit on me. _____

6. I am made of many links. _____

7. I am part of a boat. _____

8. I am an ink spot on a shirt. _____

9. I am piled in a stack. _____

10. I am used with a brush. _____

LESSON 73: Regular double vowels AI, AY

Directions: Circle the name of each picture.

sell
seal
seed

jeep
jeans
peep

bean
bed
bee

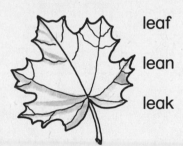
leaf
lean
leak

seal
seen
seat

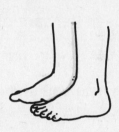
feed
feet
feel

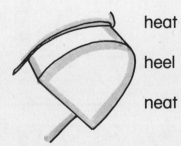
heat
heel
neat

meat
met
team

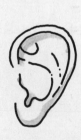
eat
each
ear

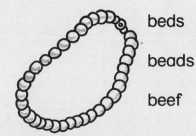
beds
beads
beef

quilt
queen
clean

deep
deeds
deer

Directions: Find the word in the list that completes each sentence. Print it on the line. Then print the two vowels that stand for a long **e** sound.

sleeve   beads   street   tree

read   meat   deer   team

leaf   seat

_____

1. Bruce likes to _____ this story.   _____

_____

2. Clean the spot off your _____ .   _____

_____

3. I'll help you string the blue _____ .   _____

_____

4. Look before you cross the _____ .   _____

_____

5. Pat has seen a _____ near the camp.   _____

_____

6. The dog ate the _____ in the dish.   _____

_____

7. The baseball _____ played hard.   _____

_____

8. This _____ has ripe peaches.   _____

_____

9. The red _____ fell off the tree.   _____

_____

10. Jean sat in the _____ next to Lee.   _____

LESSON 74: Regular double vowels EE, EA

Directions: Circle the word that belongs in the sentence. Print the word on the line. Read the sentence to be sure it makes sense.

	Jack used a _____ to dig up the land.	hay hoe hot
	Ted wore a white shirt _____ and a red _____ .	tie toe lie
	The _____ ate the grass on the slope.	die doe day
	Robby put her _____ in the cold lake.	tie top toe
	Grandma baked a _____ with fresh peaches.	pie pine pipe
	_____ can pay for a shirt with his name on it.	Jog Joe Jet
	In the fall, the leaves _____ .	doe din die

Directions: Print the name for each picture.

boat   rainbow   goat   bow   road   bowl

_____   _____   _____

_____   _____   _____

Directions: Circle the word that belongs in each sentence. Print it on the line.

_____

1. Nora rowed the _____ on the lake.   boat   soap

2. Dad used his truck to _____ the car.   row   tow

3. Please pass the _____ of fruit.   bowl   bow

4. The _____ sat on Joe's coat.   goal   goat

5. Can you _____ the ball to the tree?   throw   grow

6. Pat likes to _____ the grass.   mow   moan

150   LESSON 75: Recognizing regular double vowel OW, OA

_____

- -
_____
_____

Directions: Print the numeral of the answer in each box.

The farmer feeds the ☐ .   1. soap

Jenny's boat can ☐ on the lake.   2. sheep

A ☐ can be used to dig in a garden.   3. hay

Father said, "Use ☐ on your hands."   4. float

Baby ☐ when she broke her doll.   5. hoe

Glenn picked a ripe ☐ from the tree.   6. pie

Grandma made a blackberry ☐ .   7. paint

We will help ☐ the house.   8. cried

Farmer Gray keeps ☐ for his horse.   9. peach

Directions: Make a word to answer each riddle by adding beginning and ending consonants.

1. It fell from the tree.   ___ ea ___

2. It is something to put on.   ___ oa ___

3. A dog wags it.   ___ ai ___

4. Farmers use them in gardens.   ___ oe ___

5. We like to eat them.   ___ ie ___

6. We stand on them.   ___ ee ___

7. Seven of them make a week.   ___ ay ___

Directions: Find the name of each picture in the list at the top of the page. Print it on the line.

hoe   pie   hay   tree   leaf   boat   daisy   feet

_____   _____   _____   _____

_____   _____   _____   _____

Directions: Choose the correct double vowel from the list on the right to complete the word in each sentence. Print it on the line.

1. Joe stubbed his big t _____ .

2. I just had a slice of t _____ st.

3. Jay, may I keep your pen all d _____ ?

4. The hose sprang a l _____ k.

5. Ann broke the ch _____ n on her bike.

ai

ay

ee

ea

oa

ie

oe

Directions: Circle the correct word, and print it on the line.

1. May I sweep the _____ for you?   moon   shoot   room

2. Benny swept the steps with a _____ .   soon   broom   boom

3. Glenn had a loose _____ .   tooth   spoon   broom

4. Fran swam in the _____ each day.   cool   pool   tool

5. The lake water was _____ .   stool   spool   cool

6. At _____ we eat lunch at school.   spoon   noon   moon

7. Mary sat on the _____ to read.   stool   pool   cool

8. Jody took us to the _____ .   too   moo   zoo

9. We are looking for the _____ chest.   tool   fool   drool

10. We saw a _____ at the farm.   soothe   goose   boom

11. Do you see a man in the _____ ?   moo   noon   moon

12. The trick will _____ you.   food   pool   fool

Directions: Circle the correct word, and print it on the line.

1. Tammy _____ the plum tree.   look   shook   hook

2. Will you chop the _____ ?   wood   hood   took

3. We can wade in the _____ .   book   cook   brook

4. Tony _____ out his books.   good   took   stood

5. Put the coat on the _____ .   hook   look   shook

6. Show the _____ to Tom.   look   good   book

7. Carla _____ up and looked.   took   stood   good

8. Marty can _____ good meals.   took   shook   cook

Directions: Print the name of the picture and a word that rhymes with it.

b	h	h	w
sh	st	br	g

_____

- - - - - - - - - - - - - - - - -

Directions: Find the correct word to complete each sentence. Print it on the line.

_____

- - - - - - - - - - -

1. We wanted _____ for supper.   ready

_____

- - - - - - - - - -

2. My purse is made of brown _____ .   head

_____

- - - - - - - - - -

3. Are you _____ for school today?   bread

_____

- - - - - - - - - -

4. Grandmother needed more _____ .   sweater

_____

- - - - - - - - - -

5. Tom fell and bumped his _____ .   breath

_____

- - - - - - - - - -

6. It is cool, so you need your white _____ .   thread

_____

- - - - - - - - - -

7. When it is cold you can see your _____ .   leather

Directions: Read each sentence. Circle the correct word.

1. In the morning you eat (breading, breakfast, breathing).

2. In the big, green (sweater, weather, meadow) we saw the sheep.

3. The (head, lead, thread) in my pencil broke.

4. The (feather, weather, leather) today is cool.

5. Zeke uses (cleanser, feathers, bread) to clean the tub.

6. The box is too (ready, weather, heavy) to carry.

7. The jay left a blue (feather, cleanser, weather) in the tree.

Directions: Say the name of the picture in each box. Circle each word in the list that has the same **ea** sound as the picture name.

seat	bread
bread	beach
meat	heavy
bean	treat

reach	dream
steam	mean
break	beak
great	health

head	steak
heavy	tea
lean	teacher
steak	great

beaver	bread
team	weather
leather	seal
beans	leather

LESSON 78: Recognizing vowel digraph EA

Directions: Find the correct word. Print it on the line to complete each sentence.

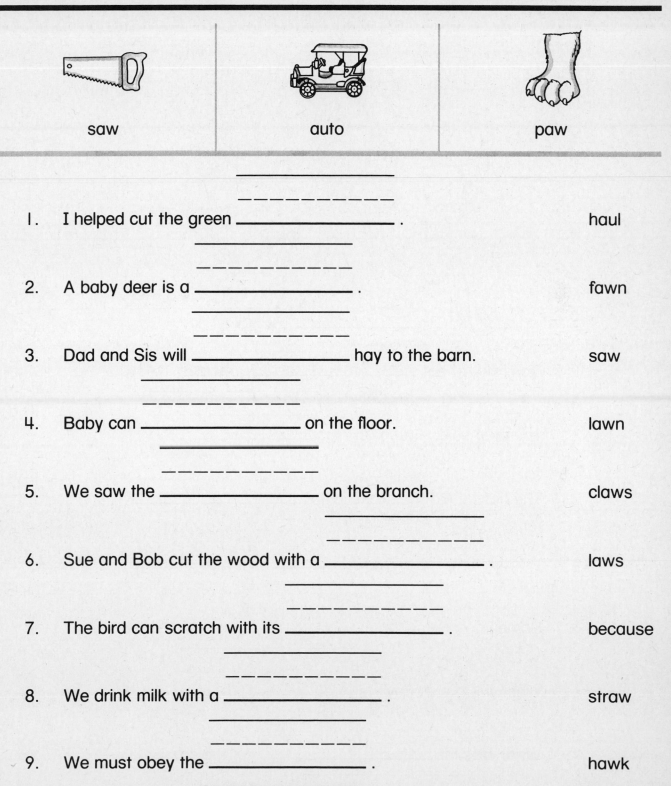

| saw | auto | paw |

1. I helped cut the green _____.   haul

2. A baby deer is a _____.   fawn

3. Dad and Sis will _____ hay to the barn.   saw

4. Baby can _____ on the floor.   lawn

5. We saw the _____ on the branch.   claws

6. Sue and Bob cut the wood with a _____.   laws

7. The bird can scratch with its _____.   because

8. We drink milk with a _____.   straw

9. We must obey the _____.   hawk

10. We left the picnic _____ of the rain.   crawl

Directions: Read each sentence, and print the correct word on the line. The words in the balloons will help you.

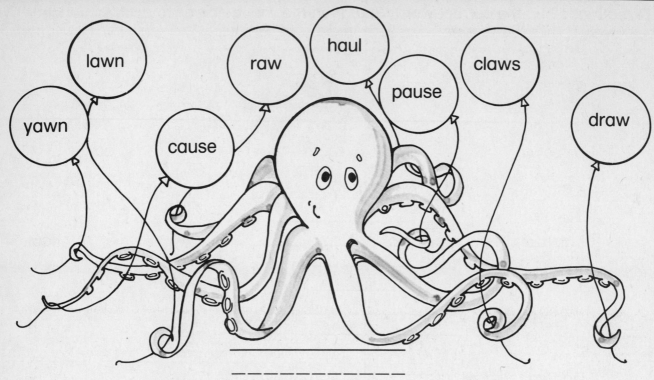

lawn yawn cause raw haul pause claws draw

1. Lions like to eat _____ meat.

2. The man said, "Keep off the _____ ."

3. The hawk held the sticks in its _____ .

4. We can help _____ away the rocks.

5. Sometimes we _____ when we speak.

6. When we are sleepy we _____ .

7. What was the _____ of the crash?

8. Paul can _____ a good horse.

Directions: Say the name of the first picture in each row. Color the pictures in the row whose names have the same vowel sound.

Directions: Say the name of the picture. Circle the letters that stand for the vowel sound in the picture name. Then print the letters to finish the word. The first one is done for you.

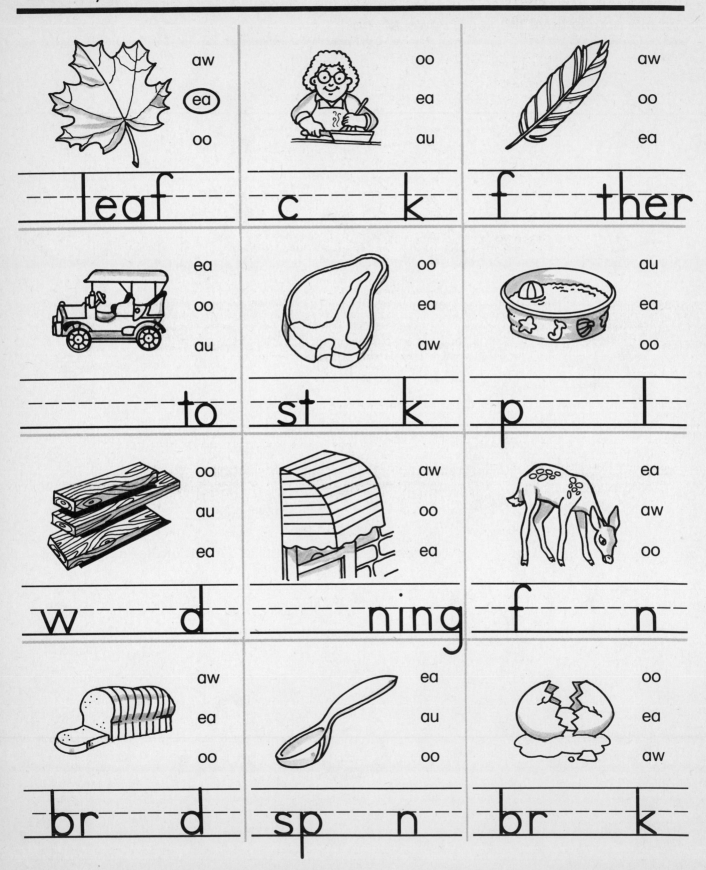

aw
(ea)
oo

leaf

oo
ea
au

c __ __ k

aw
oo
ea

f __ ther

ea
oo
au

to __

oo
ea
aw

st __ k

au
ea
oo

p __ l

oo
au
ea

w __ d

aw
oo
ea

__ ning

ea
aw
oo

f __ n

aw
ea
oo

br __ d

ea
au
oo

sp __ n

oo
ea
aw

br __ k

160   LESSON 80: Reviewing vowel digraphs OO, EA, AW, AU

Directions: Read each riddle and look at the picture. Find the answer in the list of words at the top, and print it on the line.

chair	toe	gray	pie	boat
spoon	white	bread	hook	saw

It rhymes with <u>goat</u>.
You can row it.
What is it?

_____

It begins like <u>church</u>.
You sit in it.
What is it?

_____

It rhymes with <u>book</u>.
Hang a coat on it.
What is it?

_____

It rhymes with <u>paw</u>.
You cut wood with it.
What is it?

_____

It rhymes with <u>hoe</u>.
You have it on your foot.
What is it?

_____

It rhymes with <u>head</u>.
You can eat it.
What is it?

_____

It begins like <u>whale</u>.
It names a color.
What is it?

_____

It rhymes with <u>tie</u>.
Be sure to bake it.
What is it?

_____

It rhymes with <u>moon</u>.
You eat with it.
What is it?

_____

It rhymes with <u>hay</u>.
It names a color.
What is it?

_____

LESSON 81: Reviewing regular double vowels and vowel digraphs   **161**

Directions: Circle the correct word to complete each sentence.

1. A baby deer is called a (seal, fawn, feather).

2. A low seat is called a (stool, school, steam).

3. A deep dish is called a (bean, book, bowl).

4. A dish under a cup is called a (saucer, saw, stool).

5. A crust filled with fruit is called a (pail, pea, pie).

6. A sharp tool to cut wood is called a (seam, saw, say).

7. A person who makes meals is called a (cook, shop, whale).

8. A car can also be called an (awning, auto, ant).

Directions: Print the missing letters to complete the name of each picture.

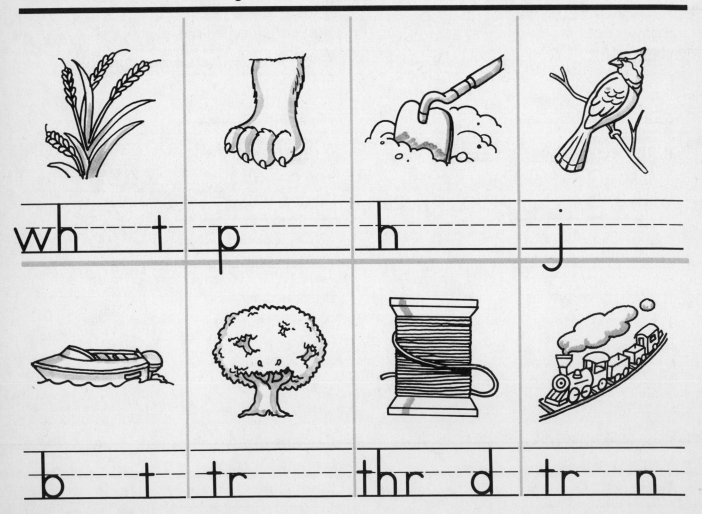

wh____   t__p   __h__   __j__

b__t   __tr____   thr__d   tr__n

Directions: Look at the picture and say its name. Find its name in the list of words, and print the numeral of the word in the box.

1. clown
2. cowboy
3. mouse
4. shower
5. howl
6. owl
7. now
8. crown
9. cloud
10. cow
11. towel
12. flowers
13. house
14. town
15. gown
16. pouch
17. shout
18. mouth

Directions: Look at the picture and say its name. Notice how its name is spelled. Find the **ou** and the **ow** words in the sentences. Print them on the lines.

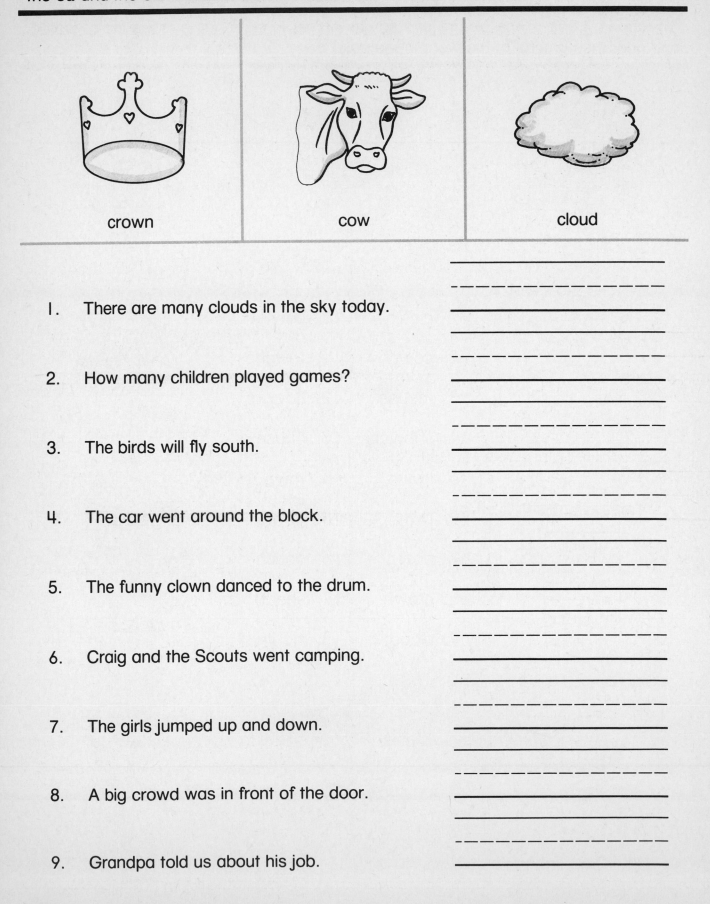

crown   cow   cloud

1. There are many clouds in the sky today.

2. How many children played games?

3. The birds will fly south.

4. The car went around the block.

5. The funny clown danced to the drum.

6. Craig and the Scouts went camping.

7. The girls jumped up and down.

8. A big crowd was in front of the door.

9. Grandpa told us about his job.

Directions: Read each riddle. Find the correct answer in the list of words at the top, and print it on the line.

owl   cow   house   clown

flower   cloud   plow   ground

1. I am in the sky.
    Sometimes I bring you rain.
    What am I?

    _____

5. You can plant seeds in me.
    The farmer must plow me.
    What am I?

    _____

2. I am in the garden.
    I am very colorful.
    Maybe I grow in your yard, too.
    What am I?

    _____

6. I have a funny suit.
    I do many tricks.
    I can make you smile.
    What am I?

    _____

3. I am wide awake in the dark.
    I hoot and howl.
    What am I?

    _____

7. You can see me at the farm.
    I eat green grass.
    I give you good milk.
    What am I?

    _____

4. You stay in me.
    I keep the wind and rain
    from you.
    What am I?

    _____

8. The farmer uses me.
    I help him make his garden.
    What am I?

    _____

Directions: Print an X next to each word in which **ow** stands for the long **o** sound.

  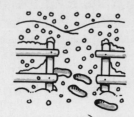 

_____ how	_____ snow	_____ gown
_____ own	_____ town	_____ crowd
_____ now	_____ bowl	_____ grow
_____ low	_____ plow	_____ power
_____ owl	_____ slow	_____ flow
_____ know	_____ show	_____ brown
_____ crow	_____ crown	_____ down

Directions: Circle each **ow** word. Then print an X in the correct column to show which sound the **ow** word has.

		long vowel	diphthong
1.	The clown fell off the big box.	_____	_____
2.	Ann tied a green bow on the box.	_____	_____
3.	The cowboy rode a white horse.	_____	_____
4.	Jim cut the pretty flower.	_____	_____
5.	Mary went downtown.	_____	_____
6.	Can you eat a bowl of popcorn?	_____	_____

_____

- - - - - - - - - - - - - - - - -

═══════════════════════════════

Directions: Circle the name of each picture.

boy
boil
bill

boy
rag
toy

corn
coil
coins

sail
sell
soil

oak
oil
out

toil
tail
toys

paint
point
pail

noise
nail
nose

came
coil
coin

Directions: Complete the sentences.

_____

- - - - - - - -

1. The black _____ train is in the big box.   coins

_____

- - - - - - -

2. I have thirteen _____ in my purse.   toy

Directions: Read the story. Circle each **oi** word and draw a box around each **oy** word.

The Little Toy Train

A little boy named Roy had a birthday. His grandmother and grandfather gave him a choice of toys. Roy chose a toy train. He was a happy little boy.

Roy enjoyed his little toy train, but it made too much noise. Roy took out a can of oil and oiled the toy. The oil made the train less noisy. It made it go faster, too.

One day Roy oiled it too much. The train went faster and faster. It rolled around the room and out the door. Roy chased it out the door and down the path. The toy train rolled up to his sister, Joy.

"Look," said Joy. "This toy wants to join me outside."

"That's my toy train," said Roy. "It ran away from me. I used too much oil."

Joy gave the toy train to Roy.

"Thank you," said Roy. "From now on I will be more careful. I will not spoil my toy with too much oil."

Directions: Use the words you marked in the story to answer the questions.

1. What was the little boy's name? _____

2. What did he get for his birthday? _____

3. What made the train go fast? _____

4. What made Roy oil the train? _____

_____

_ _ _ _ _ _ _ _ _ _ _ _ _ _ _

Directions: Find a word in the list at the right that will complete each sentence. Print it on the line.

1. A pencil has a _____ .   toy

2. Mom puts _____ in her car.   boiling

3. The water is _____ on the stove.   oil

4. Six _____ will join the coin club.   point

5. The _____ boat has a big red sail.   boys

Directions: Circle the word that will complete each sentence. Print it on the line.

1. Mary Ann will not _____ her new toy.   point   spoil   said

2. Do not put _____ near the fire.   boil   laid   oil

3. Al is going to _____ the Boy Scouts.   join   joint   jail

4. Floyd made _____ with his big drum.   nail   spoil   noise

Directions: Answer each question by circling the word **yes** or **no.**

1.	Is a penny a coin?	Yes	No
2.	Is Ann a boy's name?	Yes	No
3.	Can you play with a toy drum?	Yes	No
4.	Is oil used in a car?	Yes	No
5.	Is a point the same as paint?	Yes	No
6.	Can you boil water?	Yes	No
7.	Can you make a choice?	Yes	No

Directions: Complete each sentence by printing the correct word from the list.

1. A pin has a sharp _____ on it.   spoiled

2. We will _____ eggs for breakfast.   noise

3. The _____ little girl began to pout.   boil

4. Joyce will _____ the trip to the circus.   soil

5. The _____ found the owner of the stray dog.   point

6. The loud _____ of the jets hurts my ears.   enjoy

7. Plant the seeds in good _____ .   boy

Directions: Complete each sentence by finding the correct word in the list.

1. Sally scored a _____ points in the game. crew

2. The wind _____ the trees down. flew

3. You have a pretty _____ dress. grew

4. The grass was wet with _____ . stew

5. Many flowers _____ in the garden. few

6. We ate _____ for dinner. dew

7. The ship's _____ stopped in port. chew

8. We aren't allowed to _____ gum in school. blew

9. The gull _____ over our heads. new

Directions: Print two words that rhyme with the given word.

few	crew	grew
bl	ch	dr
st	thr	fl

Directions: Circle the word that completes each sentence.

1. Liz has a (new, drew, grew) green bike.

2. The red flowers (few, threw, grew) in the garden.

3. Grandmother gave me a (crew, few, mew) pennies.

4. Matt (stew, threw, screw) the bag to Tom.

5. We had hot beef (few, stew, flew) for our supper.

6. I need a (few, dew, mew) children to help me.

7. You must (flew, chew, grew) your food well.

8. The wind (blew, brew, new) the leaves down.

9. The baby bird (threw, screw, flew) from its nest.

10. The (crew, chew, screw) climbed into the jet.

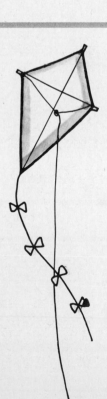

1. A kitten can (mew, new, blew).

2. Ted (few, drew, grew) a picture of a house.

3. The wind (flew, threw, blew) my new hat away.

4. Do you like to (few, new, chew) peppermint gum?

5. Who gave that (mew, new, threw) kite to you?

6. I use my teeth to (new, chew, few) food.

7. The campers saw (new, mew, dew) on the tent.

8. Mother read the (news, pews, dews).

9. Jill (threw, chew, few) a snowball across the street.

10. Jack used a (stew, new, screw) to fix the shelf.

Directions: Read each riddle, and draw a box around the correct answer word.

1. You use it when you talk.

   spoil   joy   soil   voice

2. It means that something is wet.

   round   join   moist   oil

3. You see them do funny tricks.

   crowns   clowns   browns   clouds

4. You can live in it.

   house   mouse   plow   proud

5. It is something you do with gum.

   blew   flew   chew   crew

6. It is something a dog can do.

   howl   coin   stew   new

7. A car needs it.

   joy   boil   plow   oil

8. It is something a baby likes.

   owl   toy   crowd   how

9. It is something we can eat.

   mew   drew   stew   few

10. You can bake with it.

    owl   gown   flour   round

11. It means "not many."

    new   few   dew   stew

12. It means "dirt."

    soil   coil   boy   oil

13. The farmer uses it.

    frown   plow   down   cloud

14. The cat runs after it.

    house   shout   out   mouse

Directions: Circle each **ow** word in the poem.

Just for Fun

"Moo-Moo," said Mother Cow.

"Give me my dinner now."

"Not now, Mother Cow,

It is time for me to plow."

Directions: Think of a word to complete each sentence that rhymes with the word at the right.

1. I can hear Billy shout with _____ .   toy

2. Three _____ sat in the tree at dark.   howls

3. All the robins flew _____ .   mouth

4. Our green grass was wet with _____ .   mew

5. The rain will _____ the picnic.   oil

6. The cake needs two cups of _____ .   our

7. Jane has a _____ nuts in the bag.   dew

8. The lemon has a _____ taste.   flour

9. Kate raced _____ the path.   clown

10. _____ it's time for recess.   How

Directions: Circle each **oi** word and each **oy** word.

Floyd enjoys toys.

Floyd enjoys noise.

So Floyd likes toys

That make a loud noise.

_____

- -

_____

Directions: Add **re** to each word, and use the new word to complete the sentence.

○ When the prefix **re** is added, the meaning of the word changes. It means to **do again.**

repaint
The prefix is **re.**
The base word is **paint.**

_____
- - - - - - - - - -
1. Take this clean paper and _____ your letter.   write

- - - - - - - - - -
2. Peggy wants to _____ this book to her sister.   read

- - - - - - - - - -
3. Jim will _____ the beds after lunch.   make

- - - - - - - - - -
4. I have to _____ my camera.   load

- - - - - - - - - -
5. The farmer must _____ the corn patch.   plant

_____
- - - - - - - - - -
6. Grandma is going to _____ her trunk.   pack

_____
- - - - - - - - - -
7. Now you may _____ the package for Carla.   wrap

_____
- - - - - - - - - -
8. Dad is going to _____ Nick's bedroom.   paint

_____
- - - - - - - - - -
9. It's smart to _____ your change.   count

_____
- - - - - - - - - -
10. Mom can _____ the stain.   move

Directions: Add **un** to each word, and use the new word to complete the sentence.

○ When the prefix **un** is added, the meaning of the word is changed to mean just the opposite.

The beads are strung.   The beads are unstrung.

unstrung
The prefix is **un.**
The base word is **strung.**

1. I will _____ my doll and put her to bed.   dress

2. Rick was _____ and shared his candy.   selfish

3. Arlene had to _____ the gym door for the class.   lock

4. When Burt broke his toy he was _____ .   happy

5. I will _____ the knot in the string.   tie

6. It is _____ to cheat in a game.   fair

7. The gifts lay _____ on the floor.   opened

8. The strap on my backpack is hard to _____ .   buckle

9. Fifteen is an _____ number.   even

10. Carrie was _____ of the answer.   sure

Directions: Add **re** or **un** to each word, and use the new word to complete the sentence.

1. Please _____ the story about the dragon. read

2. You'll have to wait before you _____ your gifts. wrap

3. Betty will _____ the letter. send

4. Sandy was _____ about going away. happy

5. Dale will _____ the note to his pal. write

6. It is _____ to cheat in the game. fair

7. Jack wants to _____ the grass. plant

Directions: Print the word that means the same as the two words given.

not cooked _____   spell again _____

not safe _____   use again _____

not able _____   play again _____

not kind _____   tell again _____

Directions: Add the prefix **un** or **re** to the underlined word in each box. Print the new word on the line. The first one is done for you.

to <u>write</u> again	opposite of <u>happy</u>	to <u>read</u> again
rewrite		

opposite of <u>pack</u>	to <u>draw</u> again	opposite of <u>lock</u>

to <u>build</u> again	opposite of <u>dressed</u>	to <u>fill</u> again

opposite of <u>tie</u>	to <u>think</u> again	to <u>heat</u> again

Directions: Add **dis** to each word. Use the new word to complete the sentence.

disobey
The prefix is **dis.**
The base word is **obey.**

1. One who steals is _____ . honest

2. The lunchroom was in _____ . order

3. It is unsafe to _____ traffic laws. obey

4. I _____ getting up in the morning. like

5. I _____ with what Ann thinks. agree

6. We had to _____ the wires. connect

7. The sun _____ the blue chair. colors

8. If you cheat, people will _____ you. trust

9. Gail is never _____ to her pals. loyal

10. Did Ed _____ the cave by the stream? cover

Directions: Circle the word that belongs in the sentence. Then print the word on the line. Read the sentence again to be sure it makes sense.

Mr. James will _____ the plug before fixing the TV.

discolor
disconnect

The rider will _____ and let her horse rest.

dismount
distaste

Pam and Fay are twin sisters, but they _____ on many things.

disagree
disappear

The puppy _____ its owner and ran outside.

dishonest
disobeyed

Bob loves green beans, but he _____ cabbage.

dislikes
disgrace

Ann made the rabbit _____ from her hat.

disappear
distrust

At the end of the day, the books _____ were in _____ .

disagree
disorder

Directions: Add **un**, **dis**, or **re** to each base word to make a new word.

un or dis		re or dis	
_____ please	_____ agree	_____ color	_____ able
_____ happy	_____ obey	_____ write	_____ add
_____ easy	_____ fair	_____ send	_____ like

Directions: Add **un**, **dis**, or **re** to each underlined word to change the meaning of the sentence. Print the word on the line.

1. I <u>wrapped</u> my gift.

2. Sue <u>obeyed</u> Mother.

3. Steve <u>wrote</u> his story.

4. Pat will <u>tie</u> the bow.

5. Jake <u>pleased</u> Mother.

6. The coach will <u>start</u> the race.

7. I <u>agree</u> with you.

8. It is <u>safe</u> to skate on the pond.

Directions: Choose the prefix that makes sense in the sentence. Circle it.

1. Ann will __ check her paper.   re   dis

2. Jeff __ hooked the screen door for Mom.   un   dis

3. The books on the shelf are in __ order.   dis   re

4. Luke will __ wrap the package on the table.   dis   un

5. Did you __ read the story yet?   un   re

6. I __ like riding in trains.   re   dis

7. The ice on the lake is __ safe for skating.   un   re

8. Don't forget to __ pay the dime you owe Ed.   dis   re

9. The top of Jim's paper is __ even.   re   un

10. Jean __ liked the silly TV show.   re   dis

11. Father will __ screw this jar lid.   un   dis

12. Sometimes my dog Bruno __ obeys me.   dis   re

13. Carl and Mandy will __ plant the flowers.   un   re

14. Nancy is an __ selfish girl.   re   un

15. Will you please __ fold this paper?   re   dis

16. The big storm made us tremble and feel __ easy.   un   dis

Directions: Find a word in the list that means almost the same thing as each word given. Print it on the line.

Be a good thinker!

glad   car   fast

little   ill   large

big   _____

happy   _____

sick   _____

small   _____

auto   _____

quick   _____

Directions: Circle the word in each row that means almost the same thing as the first word.

1.	**jolly**	sad	big	happy	jump
2.	**clean**	slow	funny	unsoiled	big
3.	**pile**	heap	near	rest	stop
4.	**sleep**	awake	nap	paint	read
5.	**hurt**	far	happy	sad	harm
6.	**sick**	ill	quick	lazy	glad
7.	**quick**	step	slow	pony	fast
8.	**sound**	sad	noise	find	happy
9.	**large**	huge	many	tiny	blue
10.	**close**	move	let	shut	see

Directions: Complete Peggy's letter. Find the word in the list that has the same meaning as the word shown below the line.

friend	gifts	noise	fast	kind
happy	races	easy	big	stops

Dear Randy,

_____
—————————

I'm _____ that you came to my party.
     (glad)

_____   _____
——————————   ——————————

It was _____ of you to bring those _____ .
     (nice)   (presents)

_____   _____
——————————   ——————————

The _____ book looks _____ to read.
     (large)   (simple)

_____
——————————

When I wind up the robot, it _____
                                  (runs)

_____   _____
——————————   ——————————

_____ and makes a funny _____ .
(quickly)   (sound)

                         _____
                        ——————————

                     Your _____ ,
                             (pal)

                     Peggy

Directions: Choose a word from the list at the top that means the opposite or almost the opposite of the word given. Print its numeral on the line. The first one is done for you.

1. old	8. wet	15. start
2. full	9. slow	16. last
3. down	10. hot	17. good
4. short	11. out	18. well
5. few	12. winter	19. long
6. far	13. lower	20. shallow
7. shut	14. awake	21. thick

_8_ dry	_____ up	_____ summer
_____ short	_____ near	_____ fast
_____ tall	_____ bad	_____ cold
_____ thin	_____ sick	_____ many
_____ stop	_____ upper	_____ first
_____ deep	_____ new	_____ empty
_____ open	_____ in	_____ asleep

LESSON 93: Antonyms **185**

Directions: Print the word in the list that means the opposite of the word in the box.

open	full	ill	night	float
hot	strong		asleep	sit

awake	closed	empty
cold	healthy	stand
weak	sink	day

LESSON 93: Antonyms

_____
- -
_____

Directions: Find a word in the list at the top that sounds the same as the word given. Print it on the line.

tail	here	to	meet	road	pail	heal	blue
week	cent	sail	maid	deer	pain	sea	

heel _____ see _____ rode _____

sent _____ tale _____ blew _____

weak _____ pale _____ hear _____

two _____ sale _____ made _____

meat _____ pane _____ dear _____

Directions: Circle the word that will complete each sentence. Print it on the line.

1. Can you _____ the bell ring loud and clear?   hear   here

2. Our puppy wagged its _____ when it saw us.   tale   tail

3. The _____ hid in the woods across the river.   deer   dear

4. We watched the _____ set in the west.   son   sun

5. Sam _____ his horse to the cabin.   road   rode

Directions: Find a word in the list that sounds the same as the word given. Print it on the line.

son   meat   blew   to   pane   week

heel   here   beet   cent   sea   dear

hear _____

sun _____

weak _____

sent _____

blue _____

beat _____

deer _____

two _____

heal _____

pain _____

see _____

meet _____

Directions: Choose a word from the first exercise to complete each sentence.

1. I gave her _____ of my new books.

2. The _____ was shining in my window.

3. My pal _____ me a funny card.

4. The sky is very _____ today.

5. The boat was floating in the _____ .

6. We are too _____ to lift the table.

_____
_ _
_____

Directions: Print **S** if the two words mean almost the same thing. Print **O** if they have almost opposite meanings.

first	_____	last	stop	_____	go	big	_____	large
pail	_____	bucket	quick	_____	slow	happy	_____	sad
choose	_____	pick	tardy	_____	late	bug	_____	insect
little	_____	small	top	_____	bottom	float	_____	sink
under	_____	over	unhappy	_____	sad	loud	_____	noisy
hard	_____	soft	bad	_____	good	present	_____	gift
creep	_____	crawl	long	_____	short	sweet	_____	sour

Directions: Find the word that sounds like the given word. Print its numeral on the line. The first one is done for you.

maid	3	1. sun	week	___	1. tail	pair	___	1. red
son	___	2. seem	pail	___	2. pale	read	___	2. pear
seam	___	3. made	tale	___	3. weak	beet	___	3. beat
pain	___	1. pane	deer	___	1. two	rode	___	1. ring
blew	___	2. in	too	___	2. heel	here	___	2. road
inn	___	3. blue	heal	___	3. dear	wring	___	3. hear

Directions: Circle the two words in each box that have almost the same meaning.

strike	hit	hair	stay	fast	fell
seed	shook	remain	home	quick	queen
three	tree	lift	raise	sick	snow
fat	chubby	drink	drop	ill	blow

Directions: Circle the two words in each box that have almost opposite meanings.

little	puppy	fly	fat	poor	candy
jelly	big	thin	penny	rich	good
they	fast	from	dirty	asleep	play
play	slow	clean	funny	baby	awake

Directions: Circle the correct word to complete each sentence. Print it on the line.

1. Mother made me new _____ shorts. read   red

2. Will you _____ me in school? meet   meat

3. Your _____ hat is nice. blew   blue

4. The store is having a _____ . sale   sail

5. A ship is sailing on the _____ . see   sea

DEFINITIONS AND RULES

The **vowels** are **a, i, u, o, e,** and sometimes **y** and **w.**

The **consonants** are the remaining letters and usually **y** and **w.**

A **consonant blend** consists of two or more consonants sounded together in such a way that each is heard—**black, train, cry, swim, spring, fast, lamp.**

A **consonant digraph** consists of two consonants that together represent one sound—**when, thin, this, church, sheep, pack, know, write.**

A **vowel digraph** is a double vowel that does not follow Long-Vowel Rule I—**school, book, bread, auto, yawn, eight.**

A **diphthong** consists of two vowels blended together to form a compound speech sound—**cloud, boy, oil, cow, new.**

Short-Vowel Rule: If a word or syllable has only one vowel and it comes at the beginning or between two consonants, the vowel is usually short—**am, is, bag, fox.**

Long-Vowel Rule I: If a one-part word or syllable has two vowels, the first vowel is usually long and the second is silent—**rain, kite, cane, jeep, ray.**

Long-Vowel Rule II: If a word or syllable has one vowel and it comes at the end of the word or syllable, the vowel is usually long—**we, go, cupid, pony.**

Y As a Vowel Rule:
1) If **Y** is the only vowel at the end of a one-syllable word, **Y** has the sound of long **I**—**fly, try, by.**
2) If **Y** is the only vowel at the end of a word of more than one syllable, **Y** usually has a sound almost like long **E**—**silly, funny, baby.**

Soft C and G Rule: When **c** or **g** is followed by **e, i,** or **y,** it is usually soft—**ice, city, change, gym.**

OTHER HELPFUL DEFINITIONS AND RULES

A **compound word** is a word made up of two or more words—**dog house, sand box, milk man**.

A **base word** is a word to which a prefix or suffix may be added to form a new word—**print, pack, like**.

A **suffix** is an addition made at the end of a base word to change the meaning of the word or how it is used—**printer, darkness, helpful**.

A **prefix** is a syllable that is added to the beginning of a base word to change its meaning or form a new word—**reprint, unpack, dislike**.

To make a word mean more than one:

1) Usually add **s—cats, dogs, kites**.

2) If a word ends in **x, z, ss, sh**, or **ch**, usually add **es—foxes, dresses, peaches**.

3) If a word ends in **y** preceded by a consonant, change the **y** to **i** and add **es—flies, fairies, babies**.

To add other suffixes:

1) When a short-vowel word ends in a single consonant, usually double the consonant before adding a suffix that begins with a vowel—**running, hummed, batter**.

2) When a word ends in silent **e**, drop the **e** before adding a suffix that begins with a vowel—**baking, taped, latest**.

3) When a word ends in **y** preceded by a consonant, change the **y** to **i** before adding a suffix other than **ing.—cried, crying, happily, funnier, ponies, trying**.